BIG ARMS IN SIX WEEKS

r. Universe winner Mike Quinn
ows the importance of week-by-
eek planning for building big arms.

BIG ARMS IN SIX WEEKS

by Ellington Darden, Ph.D.

A Perigee Book

Perigee Books
are published by
The Putnam Publishing Group
200 Madison Avenue
New York, NY 10016

Library of Congress Cataloging-in-Publication Data

Darden, Ellington, date.
    Big arms in six weeks / by Ellington Darden.
        p.   cm.
    1. Bodybuilding.   2. Arm.   I. Title.
GV546.5.D35   1988   87-25859 CIP
646.7′5—dc19
ISBN 0-399-51432-5

Designed by Martin Moskof Associates
Printed in the United States of America
1 2 3 4 5 6 7 8 9 10

**Other Books of Interest
by Ellington Darden, Ph.D.**
High-Intensity Bodybuilding
The Nautilus Bodybuilding Book (Revised Edition)
The Nautilus Advanced Bodybuilding Book
The Nautilus Nutrition Book
The Nautilus Diet: Ten Weeks to a Brand-New Body
The Athlete's Guide to Sports Medicine
Strength-Training Principles
Conditioning for Football
Six-Week Muscle-Fat Makeover
Super High-Intensity Bodybuilding
Massive Muscles in 10 Weeks

For a free catalog of bodybuilding books, please send a self-addressed, stamped envelope to Dr. Ellington Darden, P.O. Drawer 809014, Dallas, TX 75380-9014.

WARNING
    The routines in this book are intended only for healthy men and women. People with health problems should not follow the routines without a physician's approval. Before beginning any exercise or dietary program, always consult with your doctor.

ACKNOWLEDGMENTS
    Special appreciation is extended to the following gyms:
Gold's Gym of Venice, California; World Gym of Santa Monica, California; Gilmore's Gym of DeLand, Florida; and Gold's Gym of Jacksonville, Florida.
PHOTOGRAPH CREDITS
Chris Lund: pages 1–3, 6, 8–9, 17, 20–23, 26, 28–29, 32–33, 40–45, 47–52, 58–59, 70–71, 73, 80–81, 84, 88, 90–91, 96–98, 100–107, 110–115, 120, 124–125.
Inge Cook: pages 7, 11–16, 18–19, 118, 126.
Ken Hutchins: pages 25, 30–31, 34–39, 55–57, 60–61, 64–69, 72, 75–79, 82–84, 86–87, 93–95, 101, 108–109, 116–117, 122–123, 128.
Cliff Swan: page 10.
Ellington Darden: pages 22, 62, 121.

CONTENTS

CHAPTER ONE

The ultimate in arms would be a composite of Boyer Coe's peaked biceps and triceps (*above*); on top of Sergio Oliva's mass and bone structure (*top right*); combined with Casey Viator's forearms and rock-hard muscularity (*right*).

The Biggest and the Best

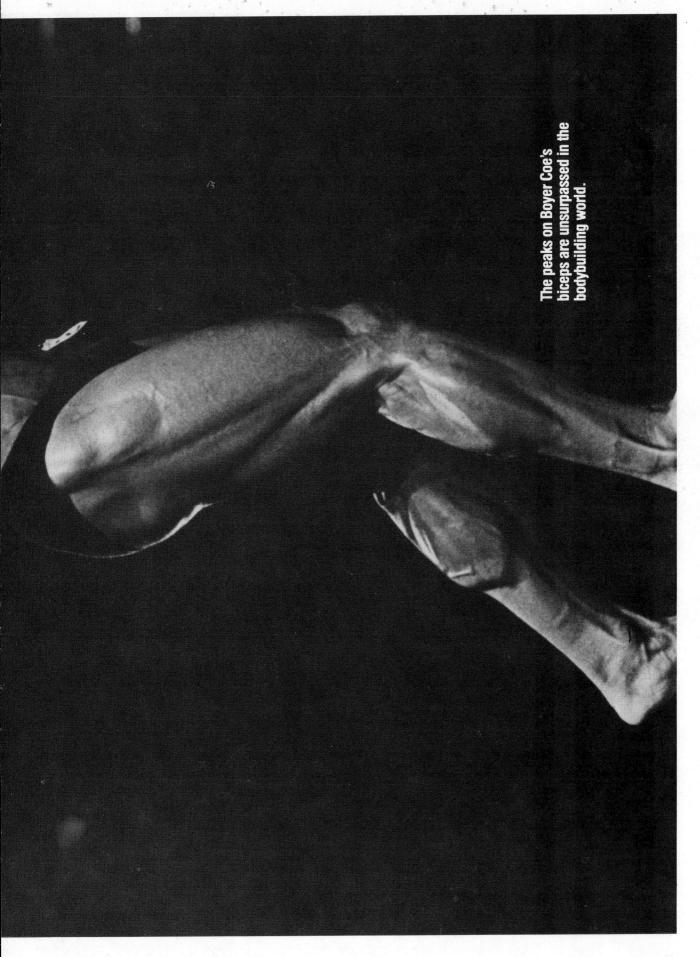

The peaks on Boyer Coe's biceps are unsurpassed in the bodybuilding world.

Big arms! I've always been fascinated by them.

Throughout my thirty years in the iron game, I've seen most of the champion bodybuilders, from Arnold to Zane, close up and in person. And I've taken a good look at the symmetry and muscle packed into their arms.

Many of them have left memorable impressions on my mind. But only three men really fall into the category of having exceptional—almost beyond belief—muscular size and shape to their arms. These three are Boyer Coe, Casey Viator, and Sergio Oliva.

BOYER COE

Of all the bodybuilders I've seen, Boyer Coe has the most dramatic shape to his biceps and triceps. His triceps are unusually long and full, which accounts for their tremendous mass and impressiveness. Boyer's biceps, however, are his trademark. One head of his biceps is long, and the other is short. This accounts for the high-peaked formation of his biceps when his arms are flexed.

Boyer's double-armed biceps pose from the front and back is unsurpassed for shape, symmetry, and muscle separation. No one has better flexed upper arms than Coe.

One fact about Boyer that many young trainees may not know, is that he was almost as well-built at age eighteen as he is now. In fact, considering the competition today, compared to what it was in 1965, Boyer was a one-of-a-kind teenage superman.

I would have gladly traded everything I owned in 1965 (which wasn't much, but it's the thought that counts), for Coe's arms. No one's arms, not even the great Sergio Oliva's, struck me with awe to match the first time I saw Coe's arms.

Left: An early Boyer Coe photo, which was taken several years before he won the 1969 Mr. America. Boyer weighed 190 pounds in this picture. *Above:* The thickness and muscularity of Casey Viator's arms are revealed in this 1970 picture.

Other people, including the judges of physique contests, must have also been impressed with Coe's arms and overall body. From 1965 to 1980 Boyer won more major bodybuilding titles than any other competitor. That in itself is a great accomplishment.

CASEY VIATOR

Casey Viator was also a teenage bodybuilding sensation when I first met him in 1969. I actually beat him in several physique contests before he reached eighteen years of age. Of course, I was also eight years older than he was and had been training a lot longer. Although I could see that Casey had plenty of muscular potential, the amazing progress that he made from 1969 to 1971 left the bodybuilding world gasping.

Arthur Jones, the inventor of Nautilus equipment, took Viator under his wing in 1970 and used him to test his new Nautilus machines and principles. At the 1971 Mr. America contest, nineteen-year-old Casey not only won the main title, but also captured Most Muscular, Best Legs, Best Chest, Best Back, and naturally, Best Arms!

Boy, does Casey have some arms.

Casey's flexed arms are very round, similar to a bowling ball. In comparison, Boyer Coe has flatter-sided arms, but with higher peaks. Viator's best arm measurement, prior to the 1971 Mr. American contest, was $19\frac{5}{16}$ inches. And this measurement was taken cold, not pumped, by Arthur Jones under the strictest conditions.

More impressive than Casey's upper arms, at least in my opinion, are his forearms. Casey's largest forearm circumference was $15\frac{1}{2}$ inches. The measurement was taken cold with the elbow straight and the wrist flexed.

When Casey contracts his forearms, the muscles swell like inflated balloons and the veins pop out like hungry eels. Even relaxed, they have awesome shape and rock-hard density.

SERGIO OLIVA

Has any man ever had the genetic potential

Opposite page: The awesome mass of Viator's $19\frac{5}{16}$-inch upper arm and $15\frac{1}{2}$-inch forearm—and at only 19 years of age! *Above:* In 1971, at a height of 5 feet 10 inches, Sergio Oliva weighed 233 pounds. Sergio won Mr. Olympia in 1967, 1968, and 1969.

that Sergio Oliva has for bodybuilding? I seriously doubt it. He has broad shoulders, a narrow waist, and a small head—all of which accentuate his wideness and thickness. And most important, Sergio has extremely long muscle bellies in all his major muscle groups.

Particularly outstanding are Sergio's biceps, triceps, and forearms. Arthur Jones measured and photographed Sergio's arms cold, in 1971, when he was in the best condition of his career, at 20⅛ inches. (Several weeks later they measured 20¼ inches.) His forearms on the same day were 15$\frac{9}{16}$ inches. Ray Mentzer, at a body weight of 260 pounds in 1983, had an upper arm measurement of 20⅜ inches, but he was much heavier than Sergio and nowhere nearly as defined.

Oliva's biceps muscles are so long that he has less than the normal range of movement around the axis of his elbow—approximately 120 degrees of rotary movement as opposed to 160 degrees in the average man. Sergio cannot bend his arms as far as most men. This has little to do with the degree of development but is the result of much-longer-than-average biceps muscles. Arnold Schwarzenegger's arm, almost as large as Sergio's, shows no signs of restricted movement around the elbow joint. Furthermore, since the greatest thickness of Sergio's forearms occurs near the middle of his forearms,

Above: The size of Sergio's upper arms, in relationship to his head, is clearly evident in this picture. *Right:* Sergio's arms easily fill up the elbow pads of a Nautilus pullover machine.

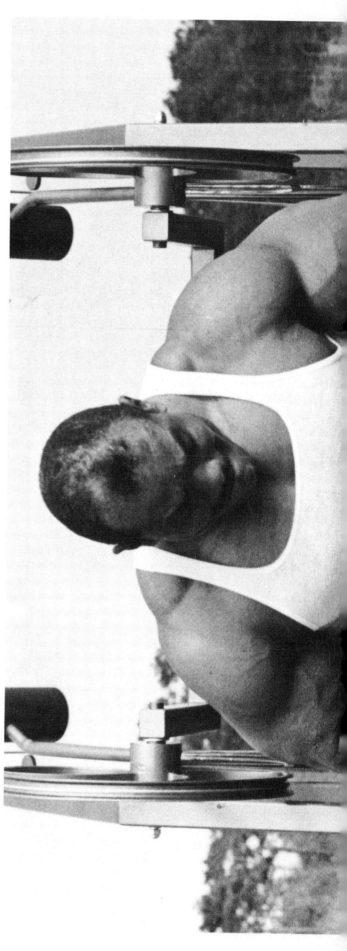

his movement is further restricted. Instead of fitting into the normal hollow of the biceps just above the elbow, the mass of his forearms meets the middle of his biceps.

Sergio's arms, therefore, are actually larger than they measure. The mass of muscle is far greater than measurement

Left: Sergio's biceps and forearm flexors are so massive that they actually limit his range of movement around his elbows. *Above:* Genetics dictates whether your arm shape will be round, flat, or peaked. Boyer Coe has a wide, flat arm with a prominent peak to his biceps.

would indicate—a result of heredity, not of training. While his training produced his muscular size, his heredity made it possible.

His limited range of movement, however, prevents Sergio from fully contracting his biceps into the high peak displayed by Boyer Coe and a few others. Sergio simply cannot bend his arms far enough to reach the required degree of contraction. It might well be that Sergio's arms would measure more than they do if they were actually less massive—if this reduction came in the form of shorter biceps and forearm flexors.

Regardless of their measurement, Sergio's arms are so big that they have to be seen to be appreciated. Some people cannot believe their eyes. In a full-length picture that Arthur Jones took of Sergio in 1971, the width of the flexed upper arms exceeded the height of Sergio's head. His arms were literally larger than his head, a size ratio never before approached by anyone.

ULTIMATE ARMS

In the final analysis, the ultimate in arms would be a composite of Boyer Coe's, Casey Viator's, and Sergio Oliva's arms. They would consist of Boyer Coe's peaked biceps and triceps on top of Sergio Oliva's mass and bone structure, combined with Casey Viator's forearms and rock-hard muscularity.

Such a pair of arms would certainly bring forth thoughts from the minds of most trainees: "I'm completely satisfied with my arms." And as any bodybuilder will admit, he's never been satisfied with his arms, *never*!

So, if you're dissatisfied with your biceps and triceps, then read on. The following chapters will tell you step by step, how to increase the size and strength of your arms quickly—in only six weeks.

Don't expect your arms to look like those of Boyer, Casey, or Sergio in six weeks. Please be realistic in your expectations.

But do expect your arms to be bigger, stronger, better shaped, and more defined. I guarantee it!

CHAPTER TWO

Top: In 1970, Arthur Jones accurately measured Arnold Schwarzenegger's upper arm at 19½ inches. Notice, however, that his left arm has less of a peak than his right arm. Arnold's left arm measures 19 inches, and his right arm measures 19½ inches. *Above:* Another shot of the great right arm of Arnold, this time from the backside. Schwarzenegger has won Mr. Olympia seven times.

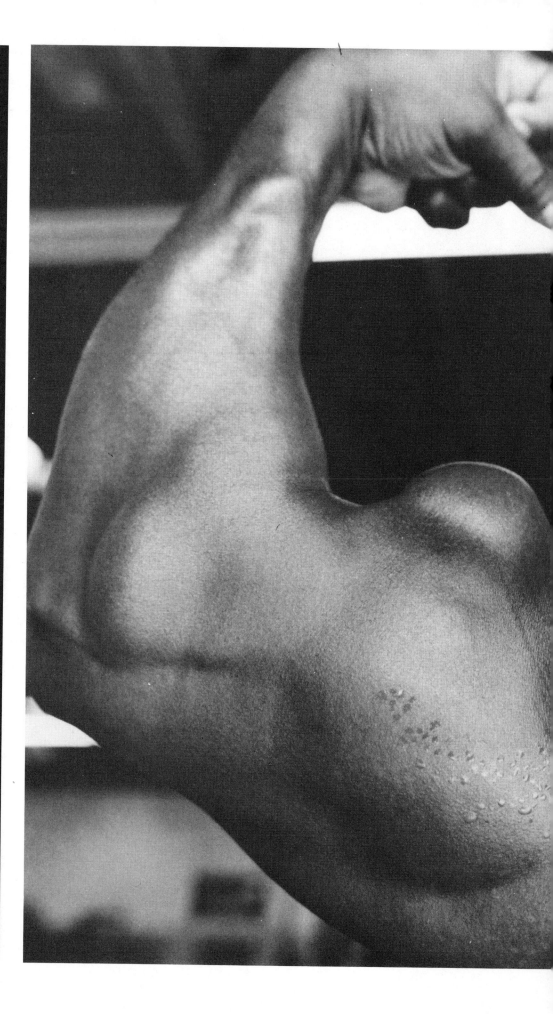

Accurate Measurements

Professional bodybuilder Albert Beckles, who is over 50 years of age, displays an unusual shape to his contracted arm muscle.

"Hulk Hogan claims a twenty-four-inch upper arm," Joe Roark said to me in a recent telephone conversation. "That's an arm as big as my thigh."

Joe Roark in 1986 had devoted an issue of his *Roark Report* (a newsletter filled with interesting muscle facts) to the exaggerated measurements that have appeared in body-building magazines. Roark is definitely the man to talk with about separating the facts from the fictions in measuring arms.

"Accurately measured," Joe continued, "a seventeen-inch arm is big. An eighteen-inch arm is very big. And anything above eighteen inches must be seen to be believed."

ARTHUR JONES'S MEASURING TECHNIQUES
Joe is 100 percent right. I've seen Arthur Jones measure dozens of arms in his I-don't-care-if-you-like-it-but-here-is-the-truth style.

First, he makes a tissue paper–thin tape out of newspaper and labels it using a steel ruler as a reference. He puts a mark at 0, 15, 16, 17, 18, 19, and 20 inches. Jones does this because he finds that with a plastic tape measure the thickness of the tape adds fractions of an inch to one's true arm size. Thus, the thinner the tape the better. He also realizes that plastic and cloth tape measures tend to shrink with age, so he always compares his tissue paper–thin tape to a steel ruler or steel yard stick.

Second, he measures the arm on the first flex. He does not let the bodybuilder pump up or contract his arm muscles prior to the taping. He wants the muscle cold, not warmed up or congested with blood.

Third, Jones reads the tape at right angles to the long bone in the upper arm with the upper arm parallel to the floor. He does not allow the tape to be slanted across the biceps and triceps.

Using such techniques, Jones accurately measured the arms of the following well-known bodybuilders at their peak condition:

- Sergio Oliva—20¼ inches
- Arnold Schwarzenegger—19½ inches
- Casey Viator—19⁵⁄₁₆ inches (This measurement was *incorrectly* stated in one of Jones's early publications as 19¹⁵⁄₁₆ inches.)
- Mike Mentzer—18⅝ inches
- Bill Pearl—18⅝ inches
- Boyer Coe—18⁷⁄₁₆ inches

A VISIT FROM MR. OLYMPIA

Several years ago, the reigning Mr. Olympia visited the Nautilus headquarters in Lake Helen, Florida. Although Arthur Jones did not measure his arm, he didn't have to. He made his point by carefully measuring Casey Viator's and my arm in front of the Olympia winner.

Casey's arm was slightly over 19 inches. My arm, at a body weight of 175 pounds was exactly 15¾ inches. Casey's arm literally dwarfed mine.

The Olympia winner, who had claimed a 19-inch arm, turned a bright red in his face. His arm, which was certainly bigger than mine, was nowhere near the size of Casey's. My guess was that this man's arm was approximately 16¾ inches, but a terrifically shaped, well-defined 16¾ inches!

Most bodybuilders in contest condition, including the champions, have arms that would measure, using Jones's techniques, 18 inches or less. But once again, a true 18-inch arm is HUGE.

Anyone who has ever seen Sergio Oliva up close is simply dumbfounded by the size of his arms. They look considerably bigger than any other bodybuilder's that I've ever seen.

COMBATING EXAGGERATED CLAIMS

I have a suggestion on how to reduce the amount of exaggerated claims that bodybuilders make concerning the size of their arms. *Allow a team of scientists, using*

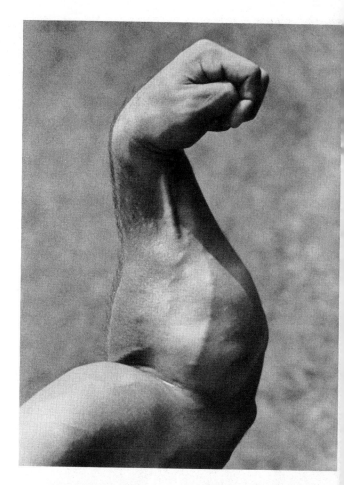

Top left: The 15⁹⁄₁₆-inch forearm of Ray Mentzer. *Left:* Scott Wilson has some of the most ripped forearms today. His right forearm measures 15⅛ inches. *Above:* Bodybuilder Eugene Laviscount of England has amazing muscularity of his arms.

Arthur Jones's techniques, to measure the arms of each contestant who enters any national contest. And most important: make certain the names and measurements get published in prominent magazines.

When I mentioned my suggestion to Joe Roark, he agreed. But at the same time he laughed.

"I'm surprised someone hasn't challenged Hulk Hogan's claim of twenty-four-inch arms," Joe said. "But believe it or not, back in the October 1970 issue of *Muscle Builder* magazine, it was reported that the pumped upper arm of Mike Guibilo measured twenty-nine inches. That's right, twenty-nine inches!"

"Yea, I think I remember the story about Guibilo," I replied. "Seems he could never be persuaded to take off his coat for a picture, much less a measurement. It's high time that the Guibilos and the Hogans of the world be forced to undergo accurate measurements."

"Right!" said Joe. "It's time to call their hands. They should put up or fold."

Whether or not true facts and figures will ever suppress the exaggerated claims of the bodybuilding world is questionable. What is not questionable is the importance of your use of accurate measurements to record the present state of your body. Understanding and applying the following measurements will allow you to chart your progress throughout the six-week program outlined in this book.

BODY WEIGHT

Record your weight on a balance-type, medical scale. Make sure that you zero the scale before stepping onto it. If it doesn't balance on zero, it may need a simple calibration. Strip down to your bare essentials and be consistent in what you wear when you weigh in. Weigh yourself to the nearest quarter pound.

The best time to weigh yourself is immediately before your workout. You can then record your body weight on your workout sheet above the date.

CIRCUMFERENCE OF BODY PARTS

It is difficult to take your own body-part measurements. You'll get more accurate values if you have a friend do them for you.

Even though Arthur Jones prefers making his measuring tapes out of newspaper, you'll be better off using the 60-inch plastic variety. When taking the measurements, apply the tape lightly to the skin. The tape should be taut but not tight. If you stretch the tape too tight, it will compress the skin and make the value smaller than it actually is. Take duplicate measurements to the nearest one-eighth of an inch at each of the described sites and use the average figure as your circumference score.

Do not pump your muscles prior to taking your measurements. Do not take your measurements after your workout. Take all your circumference readings before you exercise.

Here are the specific locations and the techniques to use.

● **Upper arms:** Stand and contract the right biceps. The upper arm should be parallel to the floor. Pass the tape around the largest part of the biceps with the tape perpendicular to the upper arm bone. Measure the left biceps in the same manner.

● **Forearms:** Stand and raise your right arm away from your body. Extend your elbow completely, make a fist, bend your wrist, and contract the right forearm muscles. Place the tape around the largest part of the forearm, perpendicular to the bones in the lower arm. Measure the left forearm in the same manner.

● **Chest:** Stand erect. Pass the tape around the back at nipple level and bring it together in the front. Keep the tape in a horizontal plane. Read the measurement at the end of a quiet inhalation of breath and then again at the end of a quiet expiration. The midpoint between the two is the correct measurement.

● **Waist:** Stand erect and look straight ahead, heels together, with weight distributed equally on both feet. Pass the tape around the waist at navel level. Keep the tape in a horizontal plane. Make the reading

Massive biceps and triceps are focal points of the male physique.

A highly defined waistline is an indication of a low level of body fat. One way to determine your percent of body fat is by using a skinfold caliper.

at the midpoint of a quiet exhalation. Do not pull in the belly.

● **Thighs:** Stand erect, heels approximately shoulder-width apart, with weight distributed equally on both feet. Pass the tape around the right thigh just below the buttocks. Keep the tape in a horizontal plane. Do not contract the thigh muscles. Measure the left thigh in the same manner.

BODY FAT CALCULATION

The bodybuilding program in this book is designed to build muscles. Many trainees, however, confuse muscle with weight. In their impatience, they consume too many calories and end up putting on fat, rather than muscle.

The easiest and most popular way to determine if your weight gain is muscle, and not fat, is to calculate the amount of fat you have on your body by using a skinfold caliper. If you have access to a caliper, use it according to the directions supplied with the device.

You may buy various types of skinfold calipers from a local medical supply house. Or you may purchase them through the mail by writing to Fitness Finders, P.O. Box 507 Spring Arbor, MI 49283.

Personally, I prefer the Lange caliper. The method I use for men entails totaling the measurements of three skinfolds: chest, abdomen, and thigh. For women, I total triceps, hip, and thigh. I then apply this total to a nomogram that appeared in the *Research Quarterly for Exercise and Sport* (52:380–384, 1981) to determine the percentage of body fat. A lean, well-defined bodybuilder will have a body-fat level of under 10 percent. Some champions eventually get below 5 percent.

If a skinfold caliper is not available to you, there's another test you can employ to monitor your body fat. This test will not provide you with a percentage readout, but will let you know whether or not you are getting leaner or fatter. This test involves keeping a periodic record of the difference between your relaxed and contracted upper arm measurements.

(1) Take the measurements before a training session.

(2) Relax the arm and take the measurement midway between the elbow and the tip of the shoulder, with the arm hanging away from the body. Record the relaxed arm measurement.

(3) Flex the arm and measure it at right angles to the bone around the largest part of the contracted biceps, with the upper arm parallel to the floor. Record the contracted arm measurement.

(4) Take the difference between the relaxed and contracted measurements.

If you are getting leaner, the difference between your relaxed and contracted upper arm measurements will get larger. On the other hand, if you are getting fatter, the difference between the two will get smaller. The reason for the difference is the fact that you *can't flex fat*. Only muscle contains contractile tissue.

Most of your noncontractile fat is stored directly under your skin, with thicker layers around your hips and midsection. When your percentage of fat is reduced, it is reduced to a greater or lesser degree from all over your body.

Thus, by keeping accurate records of the differences between your relaxed and contracted arm measurements, you'll be able to monitor your fatness. If you are getting fatter, then you are consuming too many calories— and you should cut back on your eating.

PHOTOGRAPHS

Have a set of photographs made of yourself posing your arms from the front and back; this may be the most meaningful thing you can do to understand your strengths, weaknesses, and overall improvements. Taking photographs like the ones presented in the next chapter is not difficult. But there are important guidelines that must be followed.

(1) Have your photographer use a 35-millimeter camera, if possible, and load it

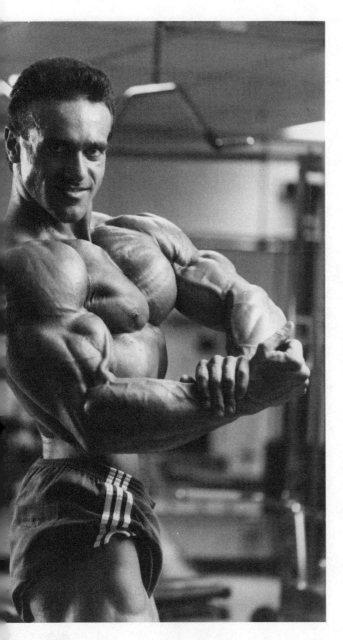

with black-and-white or color print film. He should turn the camera sideways for a vertical-format negative.

(2) Wear a snug bathing suit or posing suit (a solid color is best) and stand against an uncluttered, light background.

(3) Have your photographer move away from you until he can see your entire body in the viewfinder. He should sit in a chair and hold the camera level with your navel or, better yet, mount the camera at this level on a tripod.

(4) Face the front and ready yourself for posing. Place your heels eight inches apart. Contract your thighs and then hit a double-armed biceps pose for the camera. Turn your head toward your best arm and flex it. Have the photographer come forward for a close-up of it.

(5) Face away from the camera and do a back double-armed biceps pose. Get a close-up of your best arm from the back, too.

(6) Have a print made of each negative. On the back of each photograph, write the date, your weight, and any pertinent body-part measurement.

(7) Repeat the picture-taking session after you've completed the six-week program. Use the exact same guidelines for the after pictures.

(8) Instruct your photography store to make the image size of your "after" prints exactly the same size as your "before" prints.

PREPARE YOURSELF NOW!

Without proper measurements and photographs, you'll be beginning a six-week training program minus a good support system. Have the measurements and photographs taken *now*. You'll be glad you did, when—in a few short weeks—you start adding pounds and inches of solid muscle to your body.

How much size can you expect to add to your arms in six weeks? The next chapter describes the results of some test subjects that went through the program. Let's see what they accomplished.

Left: The muscular backside of Casey Viator as he appeared at the 1982 Mr. Olympia contest. *Above:* John Terilli contracts his muscular arms.

CHAPTER THREE

Weighing a rock-hard 220 pounds, Phil Hill won the heavyweight class at the 1987 National Bodybuilding Championships.

What to Expect

In the spring of 1987, nine men and one woman were put through the six-week program detailed in this book. All the participants were employees of the Gainesville Health and Fitness Center in Gainesville, Florida.

None of the participants were competitive bodybuilders. None of them had exceptional genetic potential for bodybuilding. But all of them were motivated to get bigger and stronger arms. And all of them had been weight training for at least six months and were in above-average physical condition.

The average age, height, and weight of the nine men was 22 years, 5 feet 9¼ inches, and 162 pounds. The woman was 21 years of age, 5 feet 2 inches tall, and weighed 129 pounds.

Below are the results of the six-week program:

The men gained an average of ⅝ inch on their best upper arm and an average of ⅜ inch on their best forearm. The woman had the same gains, also. Such improvements translated to an average body-weight increase of 4 pounds per individual. Skinfold caliper readings, before and after the study, confirmed that the 4 pounds weight gain was indeed muscle.

On the next few pages you'll see before-and-after photographs and statistics of some of the men who went through the program.

Bertil Fox, with his massive arms and excellent muscularity, has the potential to be a future Mr. Olympia.

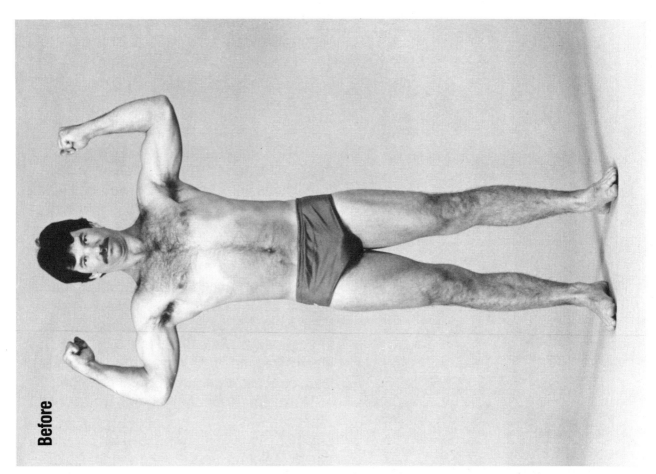

Before

Eric Seidenberg	Age: 31	Height: 5'10"	
Measurement	Before	After	Increase
Right Biceps	14¼	15⅛	⅞
Left Biceps	13⅞	14½	⅝
Right Forearm	12½	12⅞	⅜
Left Forearm	12¼	12⅜	⅛
Body Weight (lbs)	173½	182¾	9¼

After

Before

Scott Weiss	Age: 21	Height: 5'11¾"	
Measurement	Before	After	Increase
Right Biceps	14¼	14⅞	⅝
Left Biceps	13⅞	14¾	⅞
Right Forearm	12½	12⅞	⅜
Left Forearm	12⅜	12⅝	¼
Body Weight (lbs)	184¾	188	3¼

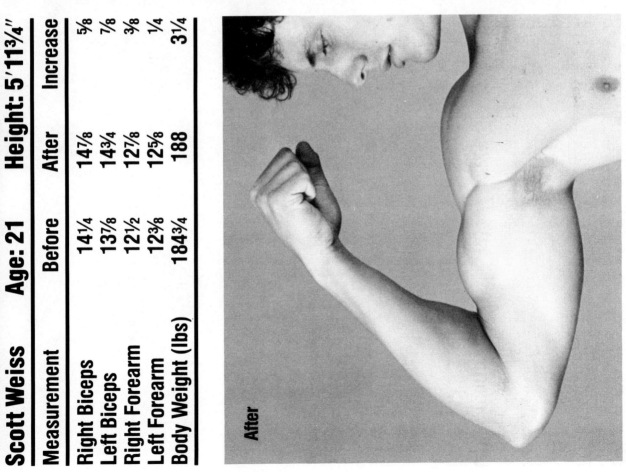

After

Before

After

Ken Cornell	Age: 18	Height: 5′3″	
Measurement	Before	After	Increase
Right Biceps	12¾	13⅛	⅜
Left Biceps	13	13¼	¼
Right Forearm	10⅞	11¼	⅜
Left Forearm	10⅝	11	⅜
Body Weight (lbs)	125	129½	4½

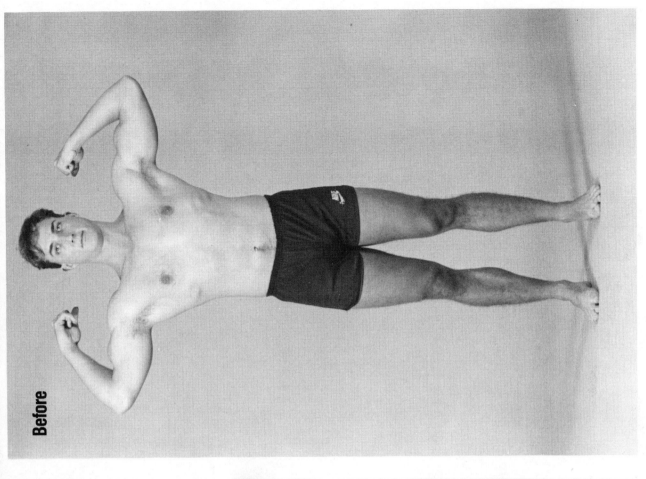

Before

Craig Halladay	Age: 22	Height: 6'1½''	
Measurement	Before	After	Increase
Right Biceps	15⅞	16⅜	½
Left Biceps	15½	16⅛	⅝
Right Forearm	12⅝	13⅛	½
Left Forearm	12⅜	12⅞	½
Body Weight (lbs)	197¼	193	— 4¼

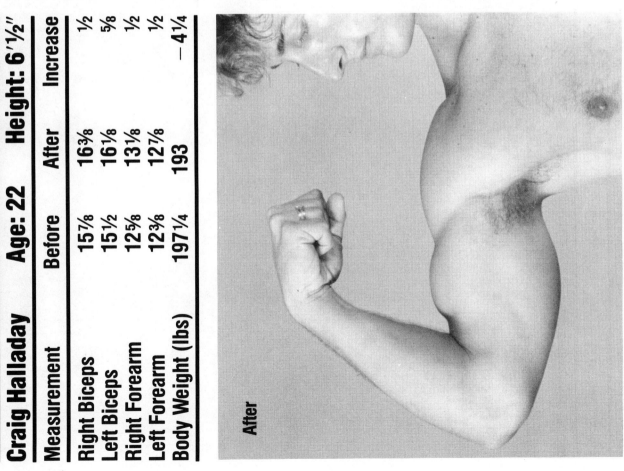

After

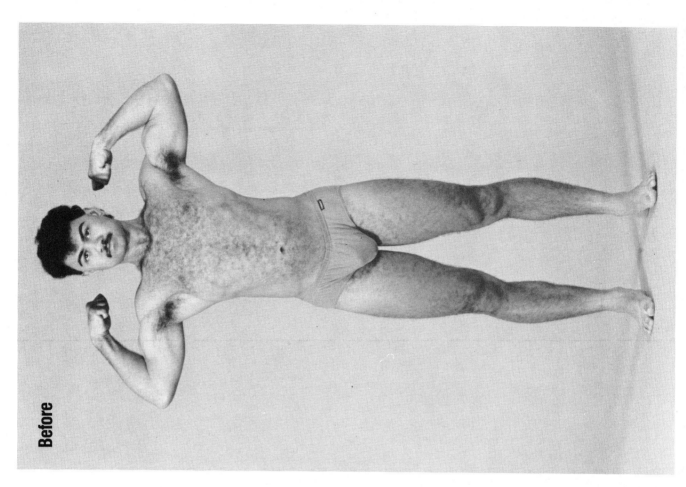

Before

Alain Watson	Age: 23		Height: 5'5"
Measurement	Before	After	Increase
Right Biceps	13⅞	14⅛	¼
Left Biceps	13¾	13⅞	⅛
Right Forearm	11⅜	11⅝	¼
Left Forearm	11⅜	11½	⅛
Body Weight (lbs)	146	146	0

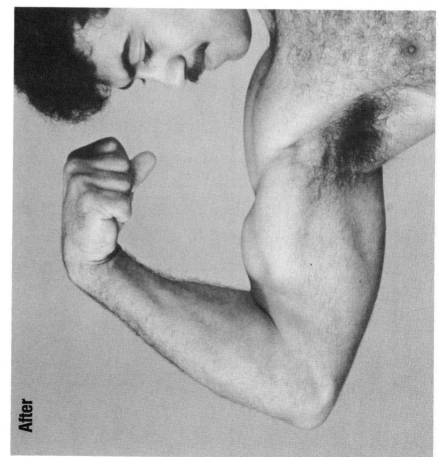

After

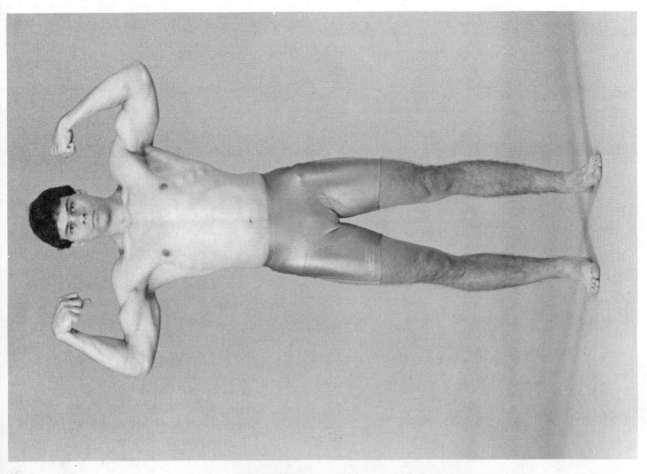

Charles Baird	Age: 25	Height: 5'8½"		
Measurement	Before	After	Increase	
Right Biceps	13⅞	14⅝	¾	
Left Biceps	14⅜	14¾	⅜	
Right Forearm	11⅝	12⅛	½	
Left Forearm	11½	12	½	
Body Weight (lbs)	157	164¼	7¼	

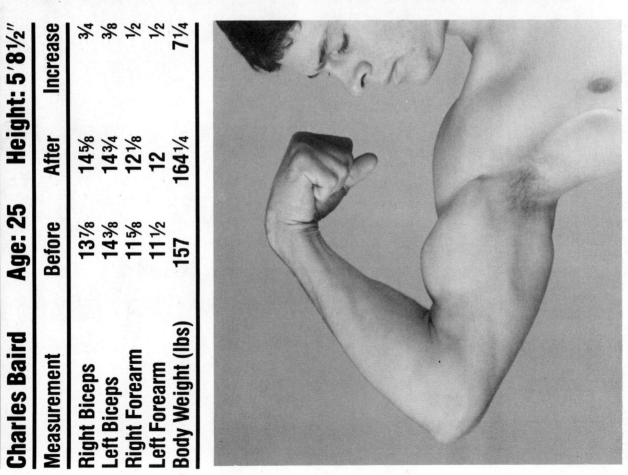

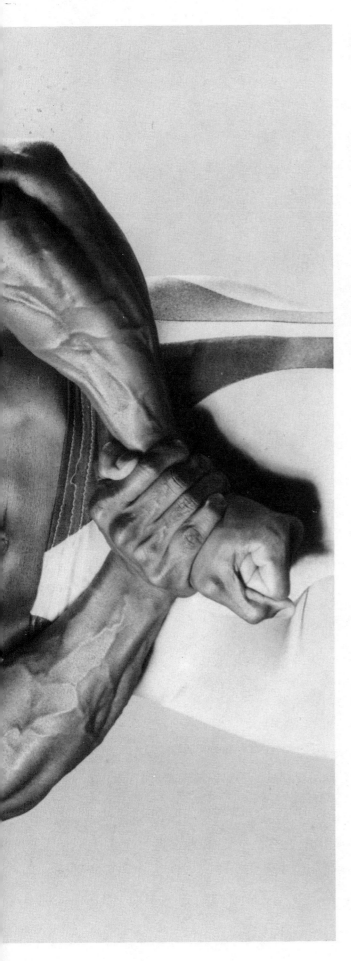

IN ONLY SIX WEEKS

Now that you've seen the results of some of the Gainesville athletes, what can *you* expect from following this six-week bodybuilding course?

If you are of average height, weight, and genetic potential, you can expect to add ⅝ inch on your best upper arm and ⅜ inch on your best forearm. If you have better-than-average genetic potential, and this component will be discussed in chapter 12, your increases may be twice that of average.

But regardless of your potential—good, very minimal, or average—you can get bigger and stronger arms in six weeks. To do so, however, requires an understanding of the basic principles of bodybuilding.

Vince Taylor has inherited long muscle bellies in his biceps and triceps, which give him a tremendous advantage in the development of big arms.

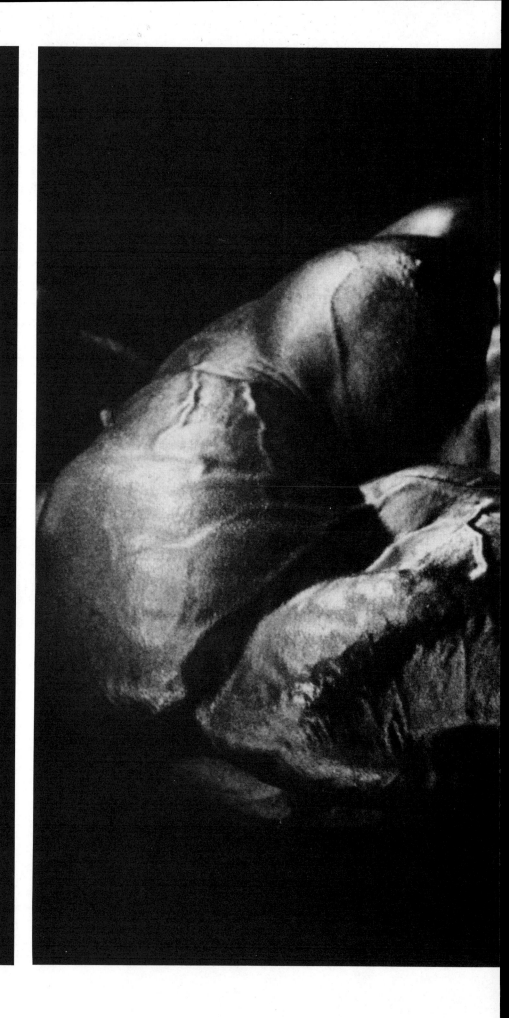

CHAPTER FOUR

The rock-hard density of Lee Haney's arm is second to none.

Principles of Bodybuilding

"Gee! I can't believe it," said Mark, a twenty-one-year-old bodybuilder-athlete. "I haven't worked out a single time in four weeks and my arms are one-eighth of an inch bigger."

It was at midpoint of the six-week program that I reported in chapter 3, and I was measuring the arms of the participants. Eric was up ⅝ inch, Kenny showed a ⅜-inch improvement, and Corrine noted an increase of ½ inch. Most of the others were up at least ¼ inch. I purposely measured Mark's arm last.

Mark, usually known as "Mr. Enthusiasm," had been going through some tough times. He had done a lot of busy work for me organizing the six-week arm program, in which he was going to be one of the participants. But several days before the program was to begin, Mark seriously injured his eye while hammering a nail into a board. He had not hit the nail squarely and it ricocheted off the board and the flat end punctured his eye.

The doctor told him in no uncertain terms that if he wanted to have normal functions of his left eye again, it would mean almost complete rest for eight to ten weeks. Absolutely no exercise was permitted, not even calisthenics. And especially no heavy resistance training or strenuous lifting. The least bit of vigorous activity might place too much stress on the delicate inner eye tissues. His eye could be damaged permanently.

At least a half dozen times Mark had asked me, "Dr. Darden, if I don't exercise for eight weeks, what's going to happen to my body?"

"You'll probably lose ten pounds of muscle mass quickly—within two weeks," I replied, judging from my past experience of working with injured athletes.

"Isn't there anything I can do to prevent

this from happening?" Mark questioned.

"No." I replied. "Just do exactly what your doctor says—and be patient. As soon as your eye has healed and you start training again, you'll quickly regain your lost muscle mass."

After four weeks of zero training on Mark's part, I was expecting to measure his arms and see a loss of ¼ to ½ inch. When the tape registered an increase of ⅛ inch, I stopped, took the tape away, checked it for accuracy, and remeasured. Again the same ⅛ inch gain.

"What's happened to your body weight, Mark?" I asked.

"I've put on a few pounds," he replied.

"Something doesn't make sense," I thought to myself, as I walked over to the water fountain to get a drink.

When I returned, Mark was in deep thought. "Dr. Darden," he said as he glanced up at me, "you don't suppose that all these years I've been overtraining?"

Then, as if lightning had flashed through the roof, I started to picture what was happening.

TOO MUCH ACTIVITY

"Mark, before your eye injury," I asked, "what was your typical day like? Give me a rundown on all your activities."

He recited a litany, telling me how he began with fifty push-ups and sit-ups each morning, with a repeat of the ritual before turning in at night. Three mornings a week he ran one mile, then quickly showered and ate breakfast before riding his ten-speed bicycle to his college classes, a couple of miles away. Late in the afternoon he'd play intra-mural sports: touch football, basketball, and softball.

As a floor manager at the Gainesville Health and Fitness Center, Mark used the club's facilities for four upper-body workouts per week.

He wasn't finished reciting, but I'd heard all I could stand.

"Sorry to interrupt, Mark," I said, "but you've listed enough already. There's no doubt in my mind. Yes! You've been over-training. Not by a little, but by a bunch.

"During the last four weeks, even though you had a serious eye injury, your body—for perhaps the first time in years—had the time to rest, recover, overcompensate, and grow. And it did—as evidenced by the one-eighth-inch improvement in the size of your arm and the gain you've noted in your body weight. We can now all profit from your unfortunate but meaningful experience."

I believe Mark learned a lesson from this situation. But because there are many body-builders who are making the same mistake, let's examine overtraining and the other physical and mental principles behind building your body in the most efficient manner.

THE PHYSICAL EMPHASIS

The key factors in muscular growth are stimulation and overcompensation. Stimulation occurs when your training is of sufficient intensity to force your muscles to adapt to the stress by growing larger and stronger. Over-compensation is directly related to your body's recovery ability.

Recovery ability has to do with the range of chemical reactions that are necessary for your body to become stronger. Although the specifics of recovery ability remain a mystery, it is medically recognized that these complex chemical reactions require time and rest. It is also known that your recovery ability does not increase in proportion to your strength.

For example, the average untrained man has the potential to increase his strength by 300 percent before he reaches his full potential. The average woman has the potential to increase her strength by 200 percent. But the potential recovery ability is dispropor-tionately small compared to your muscular strength potential.

The stronger you become, the greater the demands you are able to make on your recovery ability. In order not to erode your recovery ability, you must give your body harder, briefer exercise, if it is to be stimu-

The bodybuilding principles in this chapter apply equally to women and men. Here, Juliette Bergman flexes her award-winning arms.

lated to continue growing.

Any amount of training is a negative factor in that it drains some of your resources. The less you disturb your recovery ability, the more resources you will have available for growth. The key is to find a balance between overtraining, in which your body is too taxed to respond to the stimulation of maximum-intensity exercise, and undertraining, in which the stimulation itself is insufficient and there is no stress upon the body to adapt by growing stronger.

Thus, your training must be brief—as brief as is reasonably possible to prevent overtraining. But your training must also stimulate growth, which means it must be very intense.

● Intensity: The best way to build your arms involves high-intensity exercise. High intensity means performing an exercise to the point of momentary muscular failure. Momentary muscular failure is reached when it is temporarily impossible to achieve another repetition in correct form.

High-intensity exercise involves the greatest amount of muscle mass. Your muscle mass is composed of thousands of muscle fibers. Low-intensity work uses only some of those fibers. High-intensity exercise involves the maximum amount possible.

Building your body is a deliberate, controlled procedure. Foremost in this procedure is your ability to grind out the last several repetitions, the repetitions that are the most painful. Learning to endure the exercise's pain or burn is necessary for maximum results.

● Progression: Progression in exercise involves increasing the workload of every training session. Doing an exercise the same number of times on a regular basis does little to stimulate your muscles to grow. With each workout, try to make the exercises progressively harder. You can accomplish this by doing more repetitions, adding more resistance, or performing each repetition at a slower pace.

Experience has shown that an exercise

Above: Women have approximately two-thirds the strength-building potential of men. *Left:* Bodybuilder Scott Wilson is a believer in the *harder-but-briefer* training philosophy.

should be performed for eight to twelve repetitions. If you cannot do eight, the resistance is too heavy. If you can do more than twelve, the resistance is too light. When you can perform twelve repetitions or more, that's the signal to increase the resistance by approximately 5 percent at the next workout. Or on some exercises, over twelve repetitions is the indication that the negative phase of the exercise should be performed more slowly.

● **Form:** Your style of performance, or form, is very important if maximum benefit is to be obtained from exercise. Proper form includes both speed and range of movement.

The speed of movement must be smooth and slow. Slow movements fully tax your muscles in a safe manner. Fast movements apply force to only a small portion at the beginning and at the end of the movement. Repetitions performed quickly are both ineffective and dangerous.

● **Emphasize the Negative:** The performance of most exercise requires the raising and lowering of resistance. When you raise the weight, you're moving against the resistance of gravity and performing positive work. Lowering the weight under control brings gravity into play in another fashion. The lowering position in an exercise is termed *negative work*. During positive work, the fibers of the muscles involved in the exercise are shortening. During negative work, the same fibers are lengthening.

Negative work is more important than positive work for building larger muscles. Special attention, therefore, should be given to the negative portion of all exercises. A good rule to practice is: Raise the resistance in two seconds; lower the resistance in four seconds. It should take you twice as long to lower a weight as it takes you to raise it.

A few exercises can be performed in a negative-only manner. Chin-ups and dips can

Progression in weight or repetitions is a key factor in successful muscle building.

The size of your legs influences
positively the size of your arms.

be done by climbing into the top position with your legs and slowly lowering with only the arms. Thus, your lower body is doing the positive work and your upper body is performing the negative work.

Your speed of movement on negative-only exercise should be very slow—from 6 to 12 seconds. The slower the movement, the harder the exercise and the more effect it has on the muscles involved.

Negative-only exercise can also be performed with the help of one or two assistants. For example, with a heavier weight than normal on a barbell (approximately 40 percent more weight than you can lift for ten repetitions), the assistants raise the barbell to the top position. It is your job to lower the resistance slowly back to the starting position. Again take from 6 to 12 seconds to do the negative work.

In any exercise, it is to your advantage to strive for maximum range of movement. If the movement resulting from muscular contraction is less than full range, the entire length of the muscle is not involved in the work. Improved muscular size and strength is most likely when the muscles have been strengthened in every position over a full range of possible movement.

● **Duration and Frequency:** If the exercises are done in a high-intensity fashion using proper form, then brief workouts must be the rule. In most cases, not more than one set of fourteen different exercises should be performed in any workout. The routines in this book consist of fourteen exercises for the first three weeks and twelve exercises for the last three weeks.

Research shows that the body needs at least 48 hours between exercise sessions to overcompensate and get larger and stronger. For best results, train every other day, or three times per week.

Do not make the mistake of assuming that more exercise is better. It is not! Harder exercise is better—and the harder the exercise, the briefer it must be.

● **The Importance of Leg Work:** If you want

your arms to grow, work your legs. This is some of the best advice that a young body-builder can apply to his or her training. Intense leg work causes your entire body to get bigger and stronger.

Your body grows best as a whole. Thus, you'll get the best possible results in building your arms if you train your other body parts as well.

For four of the six weeks in this course, you'll work your legs first and your arms last. During the third and the sixth weeks, however, you'll train arms first. Working your arms first not only prevents boredom, but has a stimulating effect on them, as you'll see when you get into the program.

● **Warming Up and Cooling Down:** It is always a good idea to warm up prior to heavy exercise as a safeguard against injury. Almost any sequence of light calisthenic movements can be used as a general warm-up to precede your high-intensity workout. Suggested movements include head rotation, hanging from an overhead bar, side bend, trunk twist, and squat. Thirty to sixty seconds of each movement should be sufficient. Specific warming up of each body part occurs during the first several repetitions of each barbell and machine exercise.

A cool-down period after your workout is also helpful. After your last exercise, cool down by walking around the workout area, getting a drink of water, and moving your arms in slow circles. Continue these easy movements for four to five minutes, or until your breathing has returned to normal and your heart rate has slowed.

THE MENTAL FOCUS
Where you choose to do your exercising is an important consideration. If possible, it should be off the beaten path. You don't want unexpected friends and neighbors interrupting your workouts. Perhaps you have a spare bedroom, a back porch, or a garage. Wherever you choose to exercise, it should be well ventilated. A room that is air-conditioned and heated may prove helpful, dé-

BASIC FOUR FOOD GROUPS FOR BODYBUILDERS

Basic Food Group	Minimum Daily Servings	Serving Size	Food Sources
Meat	4–6	2–3 ounces cooked 2 medium 2 tablespoons ½ cup 1 cup	Meat, poultry, fish Eggs Peanut butter Cottage cheese Dried beans or peas
Milk	4–6	1 cup 1½ ounces 1–1¾ cups	Milk, yogurt Cheese Milk-containing foods
Fruit/Vegetable	8–12	½ cup raw or cooked ½ cup juice 1 cup raw	Fruit or vegetable Fruit or vegetable Dark green leafy or yellow vegetable
Bread/Cereal	8–12	1 slice ½–¾ cup ½ cup ½ cup	Breads: whole-grain and enriched, muffins, rolls Cereals: cooked, dry, whole grain, grits, barley, flours Pasta: macaroni, noodles, spaghetti Rice: brown or white
Other Foods	6–9*	1 teaspoon 1 teaspoon 2 teaspoons	Butter, margarine, oil Salad dressing Jellies, jams, and other sweet toppings Alcohol (not recommended)

*May be adjusted up or down depending on daily caloric needs.

Phil Hill's contracted upper arms are outstanding from all angles.

pending on where you live, but is not required. Consider foremost your need to be comfortable in the environment and your ability to concentrate fully on your workouts.

On the other hand, if you workout in a commercial fitness center, you'll certainly need to abide by their rules and regulations. Still, you'll probably be able to separate yourself from the non-serious individuals by coming in at certain times of the day.

● **Visualization:** Visualization is picturing in your mind the bodybuilding results you would like to achieve on your arms. These images help you to focus your energies on accomplishing your goals.

Be positive, but at the same time be realistic in your expectations. Picture yourself with larger, more defined arms. Establish step-by-step goals in your mind. Visualize your arms growing by ½-inch, then 1-inch, and finally 1½-inches. Increase your expectations gradually and you'll be more successful.

● **The Mirror:** A large mirror placed appropriately in your training area assists you in three ways. First, looking at your body in a mirror helps you better visualize your training goals. Second, performing most of the recommended exercises in front of a mirror allows you to isolate the involved muscles more completely. Third, training in front of a mirror is motivating because you actually see your muscles expand as they contract.

● **Progress Chart:** Keep accurate records of all your workouts. This is usually done on a card that lists the exercise with ample space provided on the right side for recording the date, resistance, and repetitions.

EATING GUIDELINES

Building muscle requires growth stimulation followed by recovery. Growth stimulation comes from high-intensity exercise. Recovery is composed of adequate rest and proper nutrition.

There is no better nutritional guideline for a bodybuilder to follow than to consume a well-balanced diet composed of several

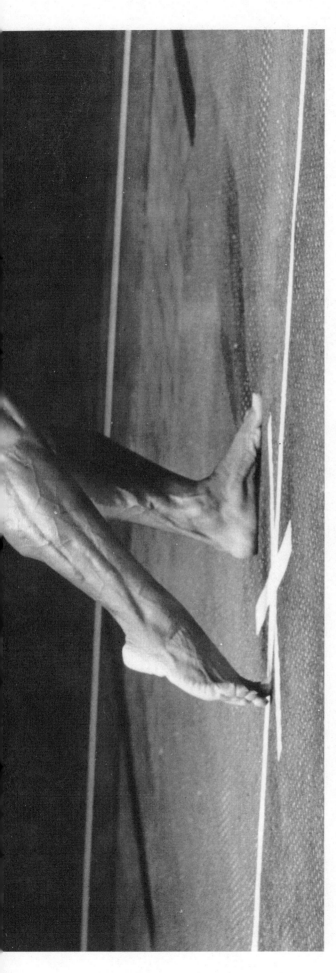

servings a day from the Basic Four Food Groups.

The table on page 54 provides food servings for the consumption of from 3,000–4,000 calories a day. The lower number of servings, in each of the groups when they are totaled, equals approximately 3,000 calories. The upper numbers added together total 4,000 calories.

The trainees in Gainesville had starting body weights that ranged from 125 to 197 pounds. They all used the guidelines successfully. The lighter participants averaged 3,200 calories a day and the heavier subjects consumed 3,800 calories a day.

To estimate the number of calories that you need per day to be well nourished, multiply your body weight in pounds by 20. In other words, a person who weighs 175 pounds needs approximately 3,500 calories a day.

One pound of lean muscle contains only 600 calories. To gain one pound of muscle a week—given that you have stimulated that amount to grow (which is not easy to do)—would necessitate approximately 100 additional calories a day above your normal level. Force feeding yourself with excessive calories will simply make you fat. Remember, exercise provides the growth stimulation; food is strictly secondary.

BIGGER ARMS NOW!

Keeping your exercise brief and very intense, and your outside activities to a minimum, will guarantee that you won't be overtraining. Applying the other principles I have discussed on a regular basis will assure that muscular growth has been stimulated. And finally, eating a well-balanced diet will keep your growing body supplied with the essential nutrients.

You should now be ready to blast your way to bigger arms!

Phil Hill's arms have almost ideal size, shape, and muscularity.

CHAPTER FIVE

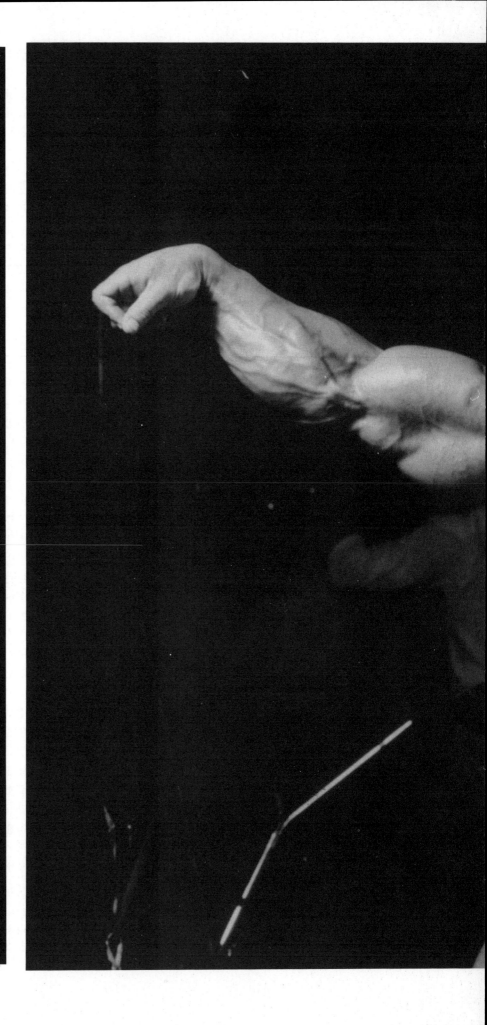

This is one of Chris Lund's favorite photos of Ed, which was taken two weeks after Robinson won the 1986 Junior National Bodybuilding Championships.

A Real 20-Inch Arm

Ed Robinson, 22, of Jacksonville, Florida, is one of the very few bodybuilders today who has a legitimate 20-inch arm.

Did the arm on the front cover of this book get your attention when you first saw it?

That arm, and the rest of the upper body shown on the back cover, belong to Ed Robinson.

The first time I saw Ed Robinson's double-arm spread, I was certainly impressed. The picture, which was taken by Chris Lund of England, was stretched across two full pages in the October 1986 issue of *Bodybuilding Monthly* magazine. Chris had taken the picture several weeks after Ed had won the Junior National Bodybuilding Championships.

"This guy is fantastic," Chris said to me during his May 1987 visit to this country. "If anybody in the world has true twenty-inch arms, and I'm as skeptical as you are about all the phony claims, Ed Robinson does. Plus, he lives in Florida."

"Aw come on Chris," I replied. "Maybe his arms are eighteen-and-a-half—or perhaps nineteen. But twenty inches! No way."

The only true 20-inch arms that I've seen belong to Sergio Oliva and Ray Mentzer. And both Sergio and Ray weighed well over 230 pounds.

"Don't take my word for it," said Chris. "Call him up, arrange a meeting, and you be the judge. And don't forget your tape measure."

I did just that.

I located Ed Robinson, managing a Gold's Gym in Jacksonville, Florida. I set up a meeting for June 10, 1987, grabbed my long-time friend and photographer Ken Hutchins, and made the required one hundred mile drive up the coast of Florida to Jacksonville.

As we pulled into the parking lot of Gold's Gym, Ed met us with a firm hand shake and a gentle smile. I liked him immediately. Ed

was attired in tight, elasticized pants, and a loose sweatshirt that was cut off slightly above his elbows. Only the bottom parts of his biceps and triceps were visible, but I could tell they were MASSIVE.

VISIONS OF SERGIO
The quick visions of Ed's biceps and triceps, as they moved about beneath his cut-off sleeves, reminded me of my first meeting with Sergio Oliva. Sergio, too, was fond of wearing loose-fitting shirts.

Sergio was in Florida and was being trained by Arthur Jones during the summer of 1971. I'll never forget the first time I saw him. He was walking the boardwalk of Daytona Beach and he was wearing a brightly colored Japanese kimono. The kimono had huge billowing sleeves that covered most of his upper arms. Each time Sergio moved his arms—and he moved them often as he talked, pointed, and waved at people—his biceps and triceps jiggled out. I just couldn't take my eyes off his huge, muscular, python arms.

Ed's arms, more than any bodybuilder's I've seen since 1971, reminded me of Sergio's.

THE MARK OF A MAN
Another thing I like about Ed Robinson occurred shortly after we met. We were sitting in the front office of the gym and I was describing some of the measurements and photographs I was hoping to take of him that day. For example, I wanted to measure his arms *accurately*, using the tissue paper-thin tape (it's actually made from a newspaper) that I detailed in chapter 2. I wanted to caliper the height of his flexed arms and compare them to the height of his head. Other measurements that I was interested in included wrists, forearms, shoulder width, and relaxed upper arms.

In other words, the typical bodybuilder who for years has exaggerated the size of his arms would promptly hide for days, if I subjected him to such precise measurements.

Not Ed Robinson. Ed didn't even wince. He was genuinely interested in finding out what his true, unpumped measurements were. Furthermore, he gave me full permission to publish the facts, figures, and photographs in this book.

Believe me bodybuilding fans: Such behavior is the mark of a mature, honest man. I take my hat off to Ed Robinson, and I admire him greatly for his attitude.

I also admire his massive arms as you'll see from the resulting measurements and photographs.

ROBINSON'S MEASUREMENTS
Before I give you a rundown on Robinson's measurements, let me mention that on the morning of June 10, 1987, Ed Robinson was not in contest shape. He was not in a ripped, tanned, shaved, oiled condition.

At a height of 5 feet 7 inches he weighed 232 pounds. That's about ten pounds more than he'd like to weigh for his next competition.

"My body weight was exactly 212 pounds when Chris Lund took the picture that's on your book cover," Ed said to me. "The picture was taken two weeks after I won the light heavyweight championships weighing 197 pounds. At 197, however, I was weak and dehydrated. I'm not planning on getting that light again. My goal is to weigh between 220 and 225 and be ripped."

In my opinion, Ed is well on his way to reaching his goal. Here's what the tape revealed on June 10, 1987.

Left: When this photograph was taken on July 9, 1983, Ray Mentzer's upper arm measured 20⅜ inches. Compare this photo of Ray's arm to the photo of Ed's arm on page 67. Notice that Ed's biceps is bigger than Ray's. Ray's triceps, however, is more massive than Ed's.

Ed Robinson's Measurements

Body Part	Inches
Right Upper Arm (flexed and contracted)	20
Right Upper Arm (hanging and relaxed)	18½
Right Upper Arm Height (measured with caliper)	7⅜
Left Upper Arm (flexed and contracted)	19½
Left Upper Arm (hanging and relaxed)	17⅞
Left Upper Arm Height (measured with caliper)	7
Right Forearm (elbow straight, wrist flexed)	15⅛
Left Forearm (elbow straight, wrist flexed)	14¾
Right Wrist	7⅜
Left Wrist	7⅜
Shoulder Width (measured with caliper)	22¹¹⁄₁₆
Head Height (measured with caliper)	8¼

Once again, all the circumference measurements were taken with a tape made from a thin newspaper and labeled according to a steel ruler. After each measurement, the steel ruler was placed beside the newspaper tape to double-check the inches and fractions.

TAPES: NEWSPAPER VS. PLASTIC

The thin paper that a newspaper is printed on has a thickness of approximately .003 of an inch. An average, plastic, sixty-inch tape measure has a thickness of .021 of an inch. The plastic tape is seven times thicker than newspaper. Thus, this extra thickness adds fractions of inches to all body part measurements.

How much does using a plastic tape add to an upper arm measurement?

Ed Robinson's right flexed upper arm, measured with a plastic tape, was 20½ inches. One hour earlier, on the first contrac-

tion of his right biceps—and using a newspaper tape—Ed's arm was exactly 20 inches. So, you might deduce that a plastic tape adds ½ inch to a 20-inch arm.

But that's not correct. During the hour between the two measurements, Ed flexed his arms at least a dozen times. He also did several exercises for his biceps and triceps. Thus, the 20½ inch measurement was not taken cold on the first contraction. Ed's arm was somewhat pumped.

Mathematically speaking, if all the factors of measuring an arm are equal—except the thickness of the tape—using a plastic tape with a thickness of .021 of an inch would add approximately ⅛ inch to your arm. And it doesn't matter if your arm is 10 inches, 20 inches, or anything in between. A standard plastic tape overmeasures your arm, or any rounded body part for that matter, by ⅛ inch.

In contrast, a tape measure made from newspaper with a thickness of .003 of an inch, would also overmeasure your arm. But the error would be only 1/50 of an inch. So technically, Ed Robinson's right arm is not actually 20 inches. It's 1/50 of an inch less,

Above: Ed Robinson's cold right arm, measured with a newspaper tape on the first flexion, is exactly 20 inches. *Right:* A standard plastic tape, because of its thickness, overmeasures your arm by ⅛ inch. Thus, Ed's 20½-inch measurement above includes a ⅜-inch pump.

$19^{49}/_{50}$, so close to 20 that it really doesn't matter.

Make no mistake about it. Ed Robinson has some of the most impressive biceps that I've ever seen. And it's not just his biceps. His triceps are unusually long and full, as are his forearms, the right being the larger at $15\frac{1}{8}$ inches.

UPPER ARM HEIGHT

One interesting measurement that is rarely discussed among bodybuilders is the height of the contracted upper arm. This distance, from the bottom of the triceps to the top of the biceps, must be taken with a caliper. The height of Robinson's right upper arm is $7\frac{3}{8}$ inches. The picture on page 67 shows the actual size (height) of Ed's right arm.

Compare your contracted arm to this life-size picture and you'll get a good idea of how big a 20-inch arm really is.

ARM-HEAD RATIO

Ed's arms actually appear larger than they are because he has a smaller-than-average-size head. The height of his head, calipered from the bottom of his chin to the top of his head, is $8\frac{1}{4}$ inches. The average man's head height is 9 inches.

Ed's ratio of upper arm height to head height is $7\frac{3}{8}$ to $8\frac{1}{4}$, or 1 to 1.12. In other words, Ed's head is slightly larger—approximately 12 percent larger—than his arms. The average man with untrained arms probably has a head that is twice the size of his flexed arm, or a 1 to 2 ratio.

The all-time king of the arm-to-head ratio has to be Sergio Oliva. Sergio, with his very small head, actually has arms that exceed the height of his head. Sergio's ratio is approximately 1.05 to 1. This accounts for some of the impact that Sergio has on people. His arms are definitely gigantic. And his small head accentuates them even more. Together, the effect is awesome.

Ed Robinson has a similar effect on people as does Sergio Oliva. Both have arms that defy belief.

I rank Ed's arms a hair below the arms of Sergio Oliva, Casey Viator, and Boyer Coe. Ed's arms do not have the peaks of Boyer Coe's, and they never will, since his genetic makeup is different. And, as of June 10, 1987, Ed's arms are not quite as massive as Sergio's, nor as rock-hard or muscular as Casey's. But Robinson's genetic potential may be such that his arms can eventually be more massive than Sergio's, and more muscular than Casey's. I'll be rooting for him to succeed.

APPLYING HIGH-INTENSITY PRINCIPLES

Part of Ed's future progress, in my opinion, will be based on his ability to apply the high-intensity training principles described in chapter 4 to his week-by-week workouts.

The routines in this course will work for Ed Robinson. In six weeks his arms will be significantly bigger and stronger.

But more important, the routines in this course will work for *you*. Big arms are only six weeks away.

Left: The height of Robinson's flexed arm, as determined by a caliper, is $7\frac{3}{8}$ inches. The height of his head is $8\frac{1}{4}$ inches. Thus, his arm height to head height ratio is 1 to 1.12. *Right:* How big is a 20-inch arm? Here is an actual, life-size picture of Ed Robinson's arm—which is $7\frac{3}{8}$ inches high on this page.

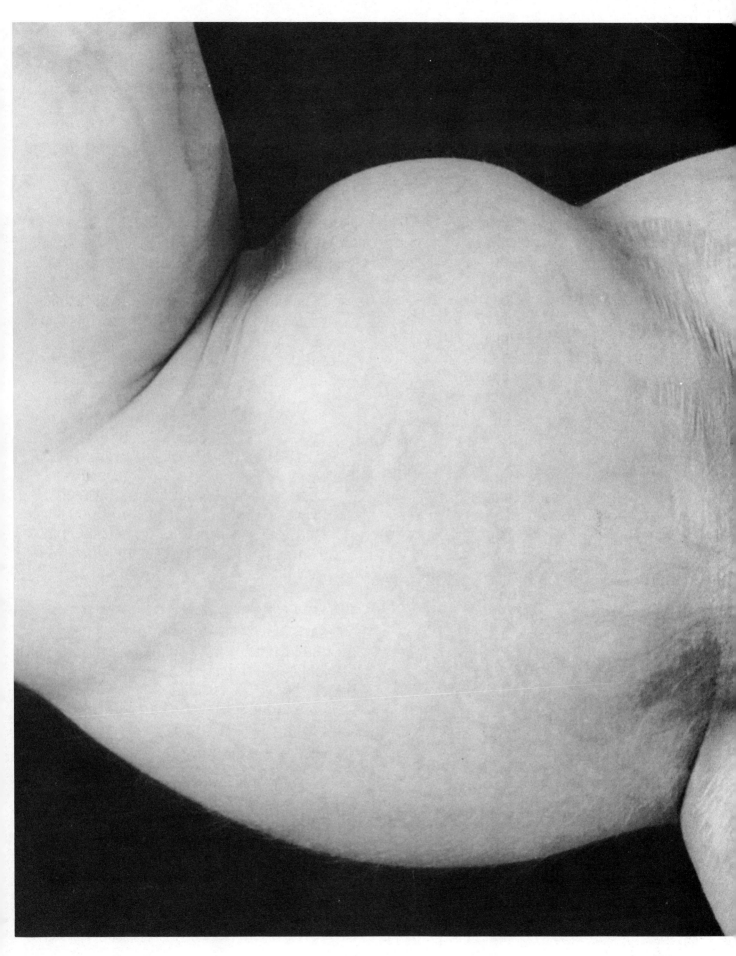

CHAPTER SIX

The massive triceps of Phil Hill, 1987 winner of the heavyweight class at the National Bodybuilding Championships.

Week 1: Getting Started

Above: Leg extension: Pause briefly in the top position of each repetition. *Below:* Leg curl: Concentrate on lifting and lowering the weight smoothly and slowly.

Tt is almost time to change into your tank top, shorts, and athletic shoes—and ready yourself for a workout. But before you do, let me say a few words about your weekly planning.

The best plan is to begin your first workout of each week on a Monday or a Tuesday. Adhere to the same Monday-Wednesday-Friday schedule, or Tuesday-Thursday-Saturday regime for the entire six weeks. This will establish an efficient pattern for stimulation, recovery, and growth.

Read the rest of this chapter, change into your workout clothes, and let's get started.

ROUTINE FOR WEEK 1

Your routine for Week 1 contains fourteen exercises: three for your legs, five for your torso, and six for your arms. Below is a listing and description of each exercise:

1. Leg extension
2. Leg curl
3. Squat
4. Straight-armed pullover with one dumbbell while lying crossways on a bench
5. Calf raise
6. Stiff-legged deadlift
7. Lateral raise with dumbbells
8. Bent-armed fly with dumbbells

Biceps Cycle
9. Biceps curl, breakdown 20%, immediately followed by
10. Biceps curl, immediately followed by
11. Chin-up, negative only

Triceps Cycle
12. Triceps extension with one dumbbell held in both hands, breakdown 20%, immediately followed by
13. Triceps extension with one dumbbell held in both hands, immediately followed by
14. Dip, negative only

LEG AND TORSO EXERCISES

● **Leg extension:** You'll need some type of leg extension machine to perform this exercise for your frontal thighs or quadriceps. Sit in the machine and place your feet behind the roller pads. Make sure your knees are parallel to the axis of rotation of the movement arm. Sit back in the seat and lightly grasp the handles. Lift the resistance smoothly by extending your legs. Pause briefly in the top position. Lower slowly to the bottom. Repeat for maximum repetitions. If you can do twelve or more repetitions, increase the resistance by 5 percent at your next workout.

● **Leg curl:** This is the best exercise for your hamstrings. Lie face down on the leg curl machine. Make sure your knees are parallel to the axis of rotation of the movement arm. Your heels should be underneath the roller pads. Curl your legs smoothly and try to touch your heels to your buttocks. Pause at the top. Lower slowly. Repeat for maximum repetitions. If you can do twelve or more repetitions, increase the resistance by 5 percent at your next workout.

● **Squat:** The squat with a barbell is a multiple-joint exercise that works your quadriceps, hamstrings, buttocks, and lower back. Using a sturdy set of squat racks, place the barbell behind your neck and across your shoulders. Step back from the racks and place your feet about shoulder-width apart. Bend your hips and knees, and lower your buttocks slowly until the back of your thighs touch your calves. Do not bounce in and out of the bottom. Return smoothly to the standing position. Take a deep breath, and repeat for maximum repetitions. If you can do twelve or more repetitions, increase the resistance by 5 percent at your next workout.

● **Straight-armed pullover with one dumbbell while lying crossways on a bench:** This is a great exercise for expanding your rib cage, chest, and upper back. Assume a supine position crossways on a bench with your shoulders in contact with the bench and your head and lower body relaxed and off the

Left: Stiff-legged deadlift: Keep a slight bend in your knees throughout the exercise. *Above:* Bent-armed fly with dumbbells: Lower the dumbbells slowly to the stretched position.

bench. A dumbbell, held on one end, is positioned over your chest in a straight-armed manner. Take a deep breath and lower the dumbbell behind your head. Stretch and return the dumbbell to the over-chest position. It is important to keep your arms straight during the movement and to emphasize the stretching of the torso when the dumbbell is behind your head. Repeat for maximum repetitions. If you can do twelve or more repetitions, increase the resistance by 5 percent at your next workout.

● **Calf raise:** You'll need a calf raise machine of some sort for this movement, or you may perform the exercise with a barbell that has been incorporated into a power rack. Place the balls of your feet on a step or high block. Lock your knees and keep them locked throughout the movement. Keep your toes pointed straight forward. Raise your heels smoothly, as high as possible, and try to stand on your big toes. Pause. Lower your heels slowly until you feel a deep stretch in your calves. Repeat for maximum repetitions. If you can do twelve or more repetitions, increase the resistance by 5 percent at your next workout.

● **Stiff-legged deadlift:** Even though this exercise is called a stiff-legged deadlift, it is actually performed with a slight bend in your knees throughout the movement. This protects your vertebrae. The stiff-legged deadlift is often neglected by bodybuilders. It strongly involves the lower back, buttocks, and back thighs. A small platform to elevate your feet under the barbell should be used to increase your range of movement. Stand on the platform and grasp the barbell with an under-and-over grip. Your feet should be under the bar. Bend your knees and lift the barbell smoothly to the standing position. With your knees almost locked, the barbell should be lowered down your thighs to the stretched position and smoothly lifted back to the top. Repeat for maximum repetitions. If you can do twelve or more repetitions, increase the resistance by 5 percent at your next workout.

● **Lateral raise with dumbbells:** This is one of the very best exercises for your shoulders or deltoids. Use light dumbbells and keep the movement very strict. With the dumbbells in your hands and your elbows locked, raise your arms sideways until they are slightly above the horizontal. Pause in the top position. Make sure your palms are facing down. Lower the dumbbells slowly to your sides. Repeat for maximum repetitions. If you can do twelve or more repetitions, increase the resistance by 5 percent at your next workout.

● **Bent-armed fly with dumbbells:** Grasp two heavy dumbbells, sit on a narrow bench, lie back, and curl and press the dumbbells over your chest. This is the starting position. Lower the dumbbells slowly by bending your elbows and shoulders. Keep your hands, elbows, and shoulders in line. Stretch in the bottom, and smoothly move the dumbbells back to the straight-armed position. Repeat for maximum repetitions. If you can do twelve or more repetitions, increase the resistance by 5 percent at your next workout.

After your last repetition of the bent-armed fly, you'll need to take a brief rest period to set up the equipment for working your upper arms. The equipment should be arranged so you can move instantly from one exercise to the next. There should be no rest between the three biceps exercises and no rest between the three triceps exercises.

Let's get ready to blast your arms to new growth.

BICEPS CYCLE
● **Biceps curl:** You'll be doing two sets of barbell curls back to back with a 20 percent breakdown in between. Load the barbell without collars so your training partner can quickly remove approximately 20 percent of the weight from the bar (10 percent from each side) after your first set.

Right: Biceps curl: Load the barbell so that the weight can be reduced quickly after the first set.

Grasp the barbell with your palms up and position your hands about shoulder-width apart. Stand erect. While keeping your body straight, smoothly curl the barbell. Slowly lower and repeat for eight to twelve repetitions. Remove 20 percent of the weight from the barbell and do a second set.

● **Biceps curl:** Grind out as many repetitions of the curl as you can in correct form. Do not cheat by leaning forward or backward. When you can no longer perform a strict repetition, loosen your form slightly and do two or three more.

Your biceps should feel like they are on fire by now, but don't rest. Immediately get to the chinning bar for the final biceps exercise.

● **Chin-up, negative only:** The Nautilus multi-exercise machine is ideal for performing the negative-only chin-up. If you don't have access to this machine, you'll have to place a chair or bench under a chinning bar. In this exercise you'll be using the strength of your latissimus muscles in order to force your fatigued biceps to a deeper level of growth stimulation. Furthermore, you'll be doing the positive (lifting) phase of the chin-up with your legs, and the negative (lowering) phase with your upper body. The positive phase should be done quickly, and the negative should be performed *very slowly*.

Place the crossbar of the multi-exercise machine in the forward position. Grasp the crossbar with an underhanded grip, climb the steps, and put your chin over the bar. Bend your knees, stabilize your body, and lower your body to a slow count of ten. Do as many ten-second repetitions as possible, usually two or three. Do several more in the eight-second range, and more in the six-second and five-second range. After each repetition, climb quickly to the top position. When you can no longer control your lowering movement, stop the exercise.

By now your biceps should really be on fire. Rest them for several minutes and ready yourself for the triceps cycle.

Above: Chin-up, negative only: From the top position, lower your body to a slow count of ten. *Top right:* Triceps extension with one dumbbell held in both hands: Lower the dumbbell slowly behind your head. *Right:* Dip, negative only: Climb to the top position of the dip, and lower your body inch by inch to a count of ten.

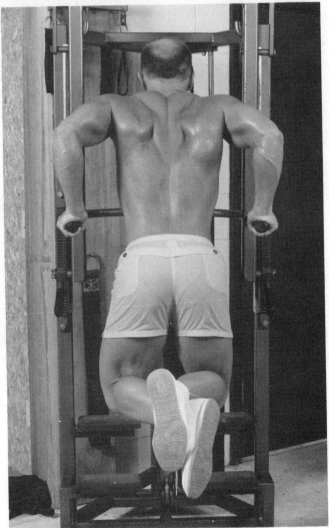

TRICEPS CYCLE

● **Triceps extension with one dumbbell held in both hands:** This is the best movement for isolating your triceps, and you'll be doing two sets back to back. You need two separate dumbbells: a heavier one for the first set and one 20 percent lighter for the second set.

Hold the dumbbell at one end with both hands. Press the dumbbell overhead. Your elbows should be close to your ears. Bend your arms and lower the dumbbell slowly behind your neck. Do not move your elbows; only your forearms and hands should move. Press the dumbbell back to the overhead position. Repeat for eight to twelve repetitions.

On the final repetition, lower the dumbbell to your chest, and place it on the floor. Immediately, pick up a 20 percent lighter dumbbell and press it over your head.

● **Triceps extension:** Do as many strict repetitions as possible. Keep the cheating to a minimum since the weight in the down position forces your triceps to stretch across two joints. This could lead to a pulled muscle if your form becomes fast and jerky. On the final repetition, lower the dumbbell to the floor and get to the dip bars.

● **Dip, negative only:** You'll perform the dip in a similar style as you used for the chin-up. If you have a Nautilus multi-exercise machine available, use it. If not, you'll have to utilize a chair beneath standard parallel dip bars. You'll be doing the positive work with your legs and the negative work with your upper body. Done properly, your pre-exhausted triceps will be ready to explode from your arms.

Climb the stairs until your arms are straight. Bend your knees, stabilize your body, and lower your body slowly—inch by inch—by bending your arms. Take a full ten seconds to lower on the first several repetitions. But climb back quickly. As you tire, the time should be reduced. Do as many repeti-

tions as you can, as long as you can still *control* your lowering. Do not simply drop from the top to the bottom. Always descend under control. And concentrate on bringing into action your deltoids and pectorals to force your triceps to a level of growth stimulation that they have not experienced previously.

YOUR BEST EFFORT

That's the routine for Week 1. Overall you've done only fourteen sets. But those fourteen sets, if they are done properly—in strict form and until momentary muscular fatigue—will provide a giant step forward in your quest for massive arms.

Give the three weekly workouts your best effort, and prepare yourself for more of the same in Week 2.

Left: Thanks to Wes Brown of Brown's Nautilus Gym, Mount Airy, North Carolina, for demonstrating some of the arm exercises in this book. *Opposite page:* Shawn Ray and J. J. Marsh compare their triceps.

CHAPTER SEVEN

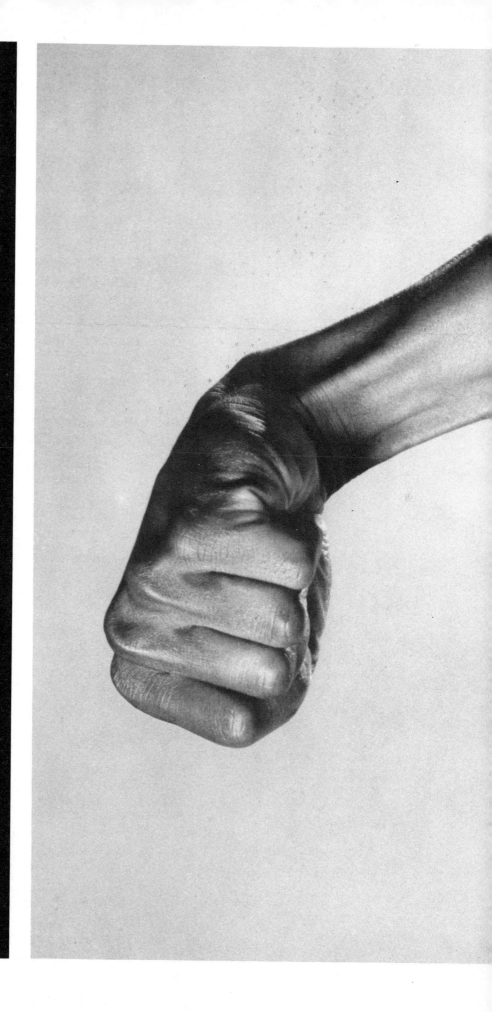

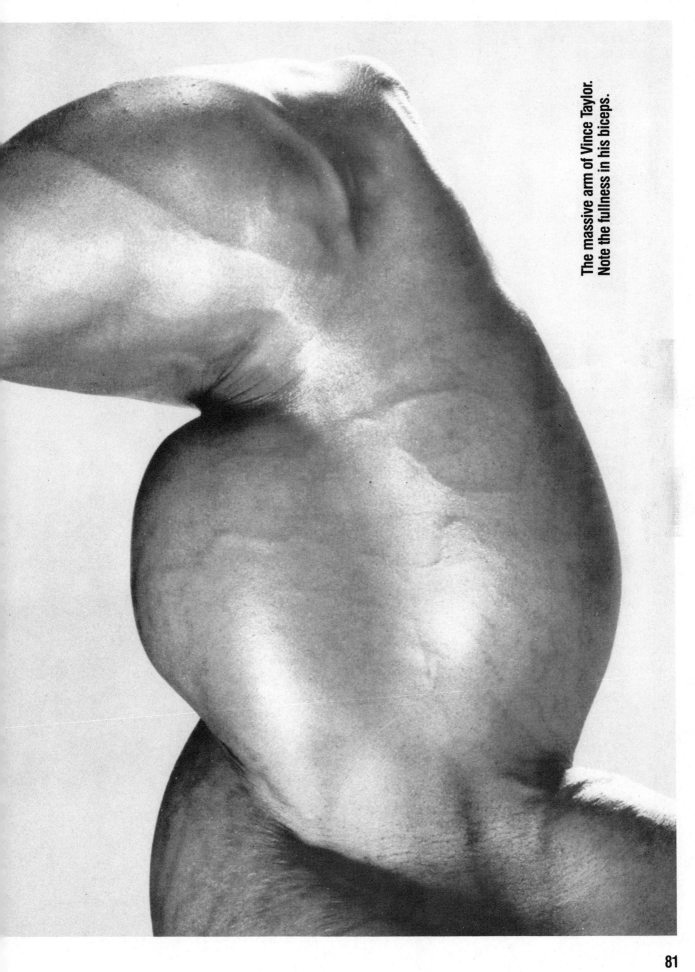

The massive arm of Vince Taylor.
Note the fullness in his biceps.

Vince Taylor has some of the best arms in the world.

Week 2: Progressing in Your Program

At the start of Week 2, you should already feel and see your arms growing. Such growth will continue each week if you progress steadily in all the recommended exercises. Make sure that each time you train you strive to do at least one more repetition in each exercise than you previously performed. Or, when you can perform twelve or more repetitions of any exercise in proper form, make sure that you increase the resistance by 5 percent at your next workout.

Progression—in repetitions or resistance—must occur during each of your workouts. There is no faster way to get bigger and stronger.

ROUTINE FOR WEEK 2

Your routine for Week 2 is similar to Week 1. Once again you'll be doing fourteen exercises. But you'll be removing two exercises from the first eight, and adding two more exercises to the arm cycle.

The exercises that you'll be eliminating are the calf raise and the stiff-legged deadlift. The new arm exercises are the behind neck pulldown and the push-up. Here's the order of the exercises for Week 2:

1. Leg extension
2. Leg curl
3. Squat
4. Straight-armed pullover with one dumbbell while lying crossways on a bench
5. Lateral raise with dumbbells
6. Bent-armed fly with dumbbells

   Biceps Cycle
7. Biceps curl, breakdown 20%, immediately followed by
8. Biceps curl, immediately followed by
9. Chin-up, negative only, immediately followed by
10. Behind neck pulldown

Top: Straight-armed pullover: Do this exercise immediately after the squat. *Above:* Push-up on floor: Turn your fingertips inward and you'll feel the movement more in your triceps.

Triceps Cycle

11. Triceps extension with one dumbbell held in both hands, breakdown 20%, immediately followed by
12. Triceps extension with one dumbbell held in both hands, immediately followed by
13. Dip, negative only, immediately followed by
14. Push-up on floor

LEG AND TORSO EXERCISES

Exercises 1–6 are described in chapter 6 (pp. 73–74). Do each of them in the same manner.

BICEPS CYCLE

Perform the first three biceps exercises—biceps curl, immediately followed by the biceps curl, immediately followed by the negative-only chin-up—exactly like you did them in Week 1. Instead of resting after the negative-only chin up, you quickly move to a fourth exercise for your biceps: behind neck pulldown.

● **Behind neck pulldown:** You'll need a lat machine, or some type of overhead pulley arrangement, for this exercise. And you won't need much resistance, approximately 50 percent of what you normally handle for ten repetitions, since your biceps will be in a deep state of fatigue.

Grasp the overhead bar with a palms-up grip. (A parallel grip is even better, if you have access to such a bar.) Your hands should be positioned slightly wider than your shoulders. Sit on the floor or on an appropriate bench. Pull the bar smoothly behind your neck. Pause. Let the bar rise slowly, pulling your muscles into the stretched position. Repeat for maximum repetitions. If you can do twelve or more repetitions, increase the resistance by 5 percent at your next workout.

Done properly, the behind the neck pulldown should leave your biceps in a state of outright shock. They will literally "have to grow or perish." Get a quick drink of water, walk around, and rest several minutes before you turn your attention to your triceps.

TRICEPS CYCLE

The Week 1 triceps cycle—triceps extension, immediately followed by the triceps extension, immediately followed by the negative-only dip—is done in the same manner for Week 2. The only change is that the push-up is added immediately after the negative-only dip.

● **Push-up on floor:** At first glance, you might think that push-ups are too easy an exercise to build your triceps. You'll reconsider your thoughts after you try them at the end of this cycle.

Lie face down on the floor with your hands directly under your shoulders. Turn your finger tips inward where they are almost touching. Your elbows should be pointing out. Do as many push-ups as you can in the normal fashion. Then, do several more in a negative manner by using your knees to assist you in getting into the top position.

If you've really exerted yourself on the negative-only dip, don't be surprised if you cannot do a single normal push-up. If that's the case, do all your push-ups negatively. Just remember to concentrate on lowering your body very slowly. Learning to relax your face and neck during the exercise will also help immensely.

TRAINING HARDER

Weeks 1 and 2 have provided you with a good introduction to high-intensity exercise—exercise that is brutally hard. Because the exercise is so hard, you should now realize that the duration must be brief.

Long, drawn out, multiple-set routines cannot be high in intensity. They must be low or moderate, or you simply cannot continue. Bodybuilders who train for longer than 45 minutes per workout are not concerned about getting maximum growth stimulation. They are merely training because they like to train!

Focus your attention on training harder. It will pay off handsomely as you progress to Week 3.

CHAPTER EIGHT

It's easy to see why Shawn Ray won the overall title in the 1987 National Bodybuilding Championships.

Week 3: Working Your Arms First

During Week 3, you'll be giving special attention to your arms by working them first. By working your arms first, you'll be able to supply your biceps and triceps with maximum concentration at the beginning of your routine, when your body is at its strongest state. Training your arms at the beginning of your routine will also add some interesting variety to your workouts.

Several new biceps and triceps exercises, plus two variations of previously used exercises, are introduced in Week 3. Two other exercises, the wrist curl and the reverse wrist curl, are done last in the routine.

The biceps and triceps cycles that center around the one-repetition chin-up and the one-repetition dip have never failed to get outstanding results. I've presented them previously in my book, *Massive Muscles in 10 Weeks*. If you've not experimented with very slow repetitions, you'll soon get the opportunity. Be prepared for a unique feeling in your biceps and triceps.

You'll only be working your upper arms twice during Week 3. The arm portion of your second training session for the week should be skipped altogether. Because of the intensity of this routine, an extra two days of recover is necessary to assure maximum growth of your biceps and triceps. You will train your other body parts three times during the third week.

ROUTINE FOR WEEK 3
Here's a listing of the complete routine for Week 3:

Left: One-repetition chin-up: Start at the bottom and perform a pull-up very slowly in 30–60 seconds.

Biceps Cycle
1. One-repetition chin-up (30–60 seconds raising and 30–60 seconds lowering), immediately followed by
2. Biceps curl

Triceps Cycle
3. One-repetition dip (30–60 seconds raising and 30–60 seconds lowering), immediately followed by
4. Triceps extension with one dumbbell held in both hands

Biceps/Triceps Cycle
5. Preacher curl, immediately followed by
6. Triceps pressdown on lat machine

7. Leg extension
8. Leg curl
9. Calf raise
10. Stiff-legged deadlift
11. Lateral raise with dumbbells
12. Bent-armed fly with dumbbells
13. Wrist curl
14. Reverse wrist curl

BICEPS CYCLE
● **One-repetition chin-up:** The objective of the one-repetition chin-up is to make a single repetition as intense and as slow as possible. Such a style of training eliminates momentum, and in doing so it serves to isolate the biceps more thoroughly. Effective biceps isolation leads to better and more complete development.

From a hanging, underhand position with arms straight, take as long as possible to get your chin over the bar. Try to move a fraction of an inch and hold, then another fraction of an inch and hold, and so on. Remain in each position briefly (without lowering) and move up inch by inch until your chin is above the bar. Have a friend who has a watch with a second hand call out the time in seconds (5, 10, 15, 20) to you as the exercise progresses. Once you've achieved the top position, lower yourself in exactly the same manner. Again,

a friend or training partner should call out your time in seconds. Begin this movement with 30 seconds up and 30 seconds down. Add 5 seconds to both the positive and negative phases each subsequent workout. When you can perform 60 seconds up and 60 seconds down, attach a 25-pound dumbbell around your waist to make the exercise harder. After this unique chin-up, run to the biceps curl.

● **Biceps curl:** Doing curls immediately after the one-repetition chin-up will reduce your strength in the barbell curl approximately 50 percent. In other words, you should use about half the resistance you would normally handle for eight to twelve repetitions.

Left: One-repetition dip: Emphasize the slowness of this exercise and your triceps will feel the stimulation clear to the bone. *Above:* Triceps pressdown on lat machine: Press your hands downward and forward.

Grasp the barbell with an underhand grip and stand erect. Curl the barbell smoothly in the strictest possible form. Lower to the bottom. Repeat in perfect form for at least eight repetitions. Loosen your form and do two more repetitions. Cheat just enough to get past the sticking point.

TRICEPS CYCLE

● **One-repetition dip:** The one-repetition dip is performed in a similar fashion to the one-repetition chin-up. Start the dip in the bottom, stretched position. Take 30 to 60 seconds to move to the top and an equal amount of time to lower. Your training partner should make sure that he paces you properly by calling out your raising and lowering times in seconds. Next is the triceps extension.

● **Triceps extension:** Because of the effect of the one-repetition dip on your triceps, you'll only need about half the resistance that you'd normally use for this exercise. Grasp one dumbbell in both hands and start performing strict triceps extensions. When you can no longer do the repetitions strictly, bend your knees and cheat two more up and concentrate on the lowering. Try to squeeze out every bit of negative strength on your last lowering repetition.

Have a quick drink of water and ready yourself for one last arm cycle.

BICEPS/TRICEPS CYCLE

● **Preacher curl:** Adjust the angle on the preacher curl bench to approximately 10–15 degrees from a vertical position. Grasp the barbell with an underhand, shoulder-width grip. Curl it and place your upper arms securely over the preacher bench. Move your elbows in, as opposed to keeping them wide. Lower the barbell to a comfortable stretch and curl it smoothly back to your shoulders. Lower slowly and repeat for maximum repetitions. If you can do twelve or more repetitions, increase the resistance by 5 percent at your next workout.

● **Triceps pressdown on lat machine:** You'll get better contraction of your triceps on this exercise if you use a parallel grip, which can be accomplished by looping a towel around the bar. Grasp each end of the towel and move your elbows to a stable position by your waist. Do not move your elbows.

Press downward on the towel and straighten your arms. In the fully contracted position, your hands should be about six inches away from your upper thighs. Keeping your hands away from your thighs when your arms are straight makes the exercise harder. Bring your hands back to shoulder level and repeat the pressdown for eight to twelve repetitions. If you can do twelve or more repetitions, increase the resistance by 5 percent at your next workout.

Take a several-minute break. As you are resting, your arms should be pumped to a degree that you've seldom achieved in the past. Shake them gently and prepare yourself to proceed with the rest of your routine.

LEG, TORSO, AND FOREARM EXERCISES
Exercises 7–12 have all been previously described (pp. 73–74). Try to progress by at least one repetition on each movement.

The last two exercises are for your wrists and forearms. Do them exactly as directed.
● **Wrist curl:** Grasp a barbell with a palms-up grip. Rest your forearms on your thighs and the back of your hands against your knees, and be seated. Lean forward until the angle between your upper arms and forearms is less than 90 degrees. This allows you to isolate your forearms more completely. Curl your hands smoothly and contract your forearm muscles. Pause, and lower the barbell slowly. Do not allow your forearms or torso to move. Do not extend your fingers. Keep the bar in the palm of your hands. Repeat for maximum repetitions. If you can do twelve or more repetitions, increase the resistance by 5 percent at your next workout.
● **Reverse wrist curl:** You'll need a much lighter weight for this exercise. Assume the same position used for the wrist curl, except use a palms-down grip. Move the backs of

your hands upward. Pause in the top position. Lower slowly to the down position. Repeat for eight to twelve repetitions. If you can do twelve or more repetitions, increase the resistance by 5 percent at your next workout.

TWICE-A-WEEK FOR YOUR UPPER ARMS
Remember, the best results on building your biceps and triceps, train them only twice during Week 3. Do *not* perform the six exercises for your upper arms during the middle workout. Work your legs, torso, and forearms, but not your upper arms.

Twice-a-week arm training during the third week will guarantee that your recovery ability will be in tip-top shape for Week 4.

Top right: Wrist curl: Flex your wrists smoothly and contract your forearm muscles. *Right:* Reverse wrist curl: Grip the bar tightly as you extend your wrists.

CHAPTER NINE

PERFECTION is the only word for Phil Hill's physique.

Preacher curl, stage repetitions: The top one-third of a preacher curl is the easiest because you are moving the weight more horizontally than vertically.

You have now completed three weeks of the Big Arms program. Before getting into the routine for Week 4, let's check your progress and compare it to the averages from the Gainesville group.

At the beginning of Week 4, you should be from 10 to 15 percent stronger on all of your exercises. For example, on the biceps curl, initially you may have done 100 pounds for ten repetitions, or 100/10. One week later, using the progression guidelines, you did 105/10. Three weeks later, you performed 115/10. Thus, going from 100 pounds to 115 pounds, with the same number of repetitions, means you are 15 percent stronger in the biceps curl. Your goal is to progress in a similar manner in all of your exercises.

If you are not 10 to 15 percent stronger in most of your exercises at the start of Week 4, then you must very simply *work harder*!

Stronger muscles are larger muscles. If your arms are 10 to 15 percent stronger than they were three weeks ago, they should also be larger. How much larger?

The ten participants in the program at Gainesville, at the start of the fourth week, had an average gain of 5/16 of an inch on their best arm. The average weight gain was two pounds per participant.

If you've gained less than 5/16 of an inch on your best arm, or less than two pounds of body weight, ask yourself several questions:

(1) Am I following the routines exactly as directed? If not, you may be neglecting an important exercise.

(2) Am I moving very quickly between the exercises that compose the biceps cycles and the triceps cycles? Taking longer than three seconds rest between these exercises destroys the pre-exhaustion effect and your results will be less significant.

(3) Am I being pushed to momentary muscular fatigue on all my exercises? If not, then your muscles are not being stimulated to grow in the most efficient manner.

(4) Am I getting adequate rest and relaxation between my workouts? For building maximum muscle mass, it's a good idea to keep other fitness activities—such as jogging, tennis, and cycling—to a bare minimum.

(5) Am I eating the recommended servings each day from the Basic Four Food Groups? If not, you may be getting an inadequate ratio of muscle-building calories.

ROUTINE FOR WEEK 4

For Week 4, as well as for Weeks 5 and 6, the number of exercises are reduced from fourteen to twelve. As you get stronger in all your exercises, your body makes progressively deeper inroads into your recovery ability. Thus, to continue to make the same rate of progress, you have to perform less overall exercise.

Here's a listing of the routine for Week 4:

1. Leg extension
2. Leg curl
3. Squat
4. Straight-armed pullover with one dumbbell while lying crossways on a bench
5. Calf raise
6. Bent-armed fly with dumbbells

Biceps Cycle
7. Preacher curl, stage repetitions, immediately followed by
8. Alternate dumbbell curl

Triceps Cycle
9. Triceps pressdown on lat machine, stage repetitions, immediately followed by
10. L-seat dip

Biceps/Triceps Cycle
11. Behind neck pulldown
12. Close grip bench press

LEG AND TORSO EXERCISES

Exercises 1–6 are performed in the same manner as previously described (pp. 71–74). If you need help with these exercises, turn back to chapter 6.

BICEPS CYCLE

● **Preacher curl, stage repetitions:** Divide the curl into three stages: bottom, middle, and top. In the preacher curl, the bottom position, because of gravitational forces, is the hardest, the middle is the next hardest, and the top is the easiest.

Grasp the barbell with an underhanded, shoulder-width grip. Curl it and place your upper arms securely over the preacher bench. Move your elbows in as opposed to keeping them wide. Lower the barbell to a comfortable stretch and curl it only one-third of the way up and stop. Lower to the bottom and continue curling in the bottom one-third of the movement for ten repetitions.

On the last repetition, curl the barbell two-thirds the way up. Stop and lower one-third the way down. Continue curling in the middle range for ten repetitions.

On the last repetition, curl the barbell to the top position. Now lower and raise it only in the top one-third of the movement. Continue for another ten partial-range repetitions. When you can do twelve or more partial-range repetitions in all three stages, increase the resistance by 5 percent at your next workout.

● **Alternate dumbbell curl:** Grasp a moderately heavy dumbbell in each hand. Curl the left dumbbell to your shoulder. As you lower the left dumbbell, start curling the right. With a little practice, you should be lifting one dumbbell while the other one is lowering. Continue for maximum repetitions. If you can do twelve or more repetitions, increase the resistance by 5 percent at your next workout.

TRICEPS CYCLE

● **Triceps pressdown on lat machine, stage repetitions:** In the triceps pressdown, the bottom stage is the hardest, the middle stage is the next hardest, and the top stage is the easiest.

Press downward on the towel and straighten your arms. Bring your hands one-third of the way back and stop. Press downward and continue working the bottom stage for ten repetitions.

On the last repetition, bring your hands two-thirds the way up and stop. Work only the middle one-third of the range for ten repetitions. Get another ten partial-range repetitions in the top one-third of the movement. When you can do twelve or more partial-range repetitions in all three stages, increase the resistance by 5 percent at your next workout.

● **L-seat dip:** Sit on the side of a bench. Place your hands by your hips with your fingers just off the edge. Now put both your feet on top of another bench, or chair, which is located in front of you, approximately three to four feet away. Viewed from the side, your torso and legs form the letter *L*.

Bend your arms and let your buttocks almost touch the floor. Push back to the top position. Repeat for maximum repetitions. If you can perform twelve or more repetitions, place a barbell plate on your lap at your next workout.

BICEPS/TRICEPS CYCLE

● **Behind neck pulldown:** Grasp the over-head bar of a lat machine with a palms-up grip. Sit on the floor or on an appropriate bench. Pull the bar smoothly behind your neck. Pause. Let the bar rise slowly to the stretched position. Repeat for maximum repetitions. If you can do twelve or more repetitions, increase the resistance by 5 percent at your next workout.

● **Close-grip bench press:** Lie on a flat bench. Grasp a barbell with your hands approximately six inches apart. Lower the barbell to your sternum and press it back over your chest. Repeat for maximum repetitions, increase the resistance by 5 percent at your next workout.

MOVING FORWARD

The routine for Week 4 sets the stage for next week's schedule. Give the three workouts in Week 4 your maximum attention and your arms will continue to grow to new heights.

Above: Triceps pressdown on lat machine, stage repetitions: Note that the hands are away from the body in the extended position. This makes the exercise harder and more productive. *Top right:* L-seat dip: Lower your body until your buttocks almost touch the floor. *Right:* Close-grip bench press: Do not initiate the movement of the bar off your chest with a jerk. Keep the movement controlled.

CHAPTER TEN

Mike Quinn attacks his deltoids and triceps with a set of behind-neck presses.

Excessive arching of the back in the performance of seated dumbbell curls is a form of cheating. Such cheating does not contribute to growth stimulation, and it is dangerous.

There is a tendency for many bodybuilders to become sloppy in their training during the fifth week of almost any six-week program. Sloppy training usually means there's a slow degeneration of the style of performance of each exercise. Let's examine this factor and discuss what can be done to combat it.

STYLE OF PERFORMANCE

Numerous bodybuilders, in their attempt to demonstrate strength, loosen their form and actually provide less stimulation to the desired muscle group. Sure, they handle more weight. But in doing so they bring into action other muscles that do not contribute to the isolation of the targeted muscle.

Do not make the common error of performing your workouts in such a manner that you can handle as much weight as possible. Instead, make the work as hard as possible for the muscles you are trying to stimulate. Don't look for ways to make your exercises easier so that you can handle more weight. Look for ways to make every exercise as hard as you can. Performed in one way, you may be able to use 200 pounds in a particular exercise. Performed in another way, the same exercise may produce far better results with only 100 pounds of resistance.

You should perform as much resistance as possible and you should perform as many repetitions as momentarily possible—but not if increasing the resistance or the number of repetitions results in a relaxation of style.

Relaxation of style often signals that both the lifting and the lowering phases of your repetitions are done too quickly. A quick jerk at the beginning of any repetition means that you are throwing the weight through much of the middle range of the movement. Not only is this unproductive on the muscle, but it is dangerous. It is dangerous at the start because a sudden jerk can tear a muscle. Also, it is dangerous at the end of the movement because now you have to stop the movement of the weight with another forceful jerk.

In chapter 4, I discussed an important guideline that applies to almost every repetition: *Raise the resistance in two seconds; lower the resistance in four seconds.*

At first glance, two seconds up may seem fast. But in fact, it is slow—at least from a working muscle's viewpoint.

Count to yourself as you start an exercise: one thousand and one, one thousand and two. Pause. As you begin to lower, count to four: one thousand and one, one thousand and two, one thousand and three, one thousand and four.

Done in this format, two seconds up and four seconds down is *slow*, which is exactly what a repetition should be to produce maximum muscular stimulation.

Decide now that in all your exercises for Week 5 you'll practice a slow, smooth speed of movement. You'll be glad you did when you see the effects that such training will have on your arms.

ROUTINE FOR WEEK 5
Here are the twelve exercises that you'll be doing for this week:

1. Leg extension
2. Leg curl
3. Squat
4. Straight-armed pullover with one dumbbell while lying crossways on a bench
5. Stiff-legged deadlift
6. Lateral raise with dumbbells

Biceps Cycle
7. Preacher curl, immediately followed by
8. Alternate dumbbell curl

Triceps Cycle
9. Triceps pressdown on lat machine, immediately followed by
10. L-seat dip

Biceps/Triceps Cycle
11. Chin-up, negative only
12. Dip, negative only

Victor Richards's relaxed arms look big from all angles.

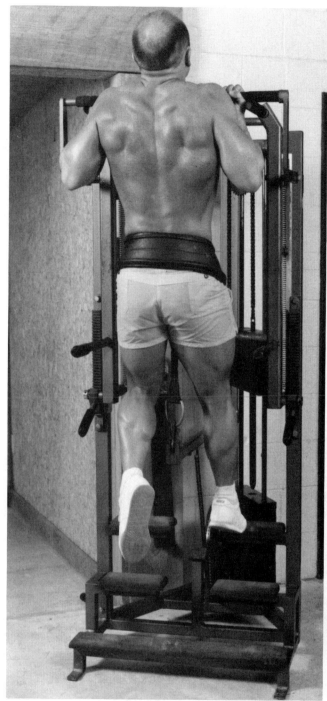

Alternate dumbbell curl: This exercise can be performed sitting or standing.

Chin-up, negative only: Climb up quickly to the top position, take your feet away, and lower your body slowly to the bottom.

Dip, negative only: Since your negative strength is 40 percent stronger than your positive strength, don't be afraid to add extra resistance around your waist.

LEG AND TORSO EXERCISES

In Week 5 you'll substitute the stiff-legged deadlift for the calf raise, and the lateral raise for the bent-armed fly. Both of these movements and the other leg and torso exercises have been previously described in earlier chapters.

BICEPS CYCLE

You'll be performing the preacher curl in the normal manner (not stage repetitions), immediately followed by the alternate dumbbell curl. Do them exactly as I described them in chapters 8 and 9. (See pp. 91 and 99.)

TRICEPS CYCLE

The triceps cycle consists of two exercises, the triceps pressdown and the L-seat dip, that have also been used before. Turn back to chapters 8 and 9 for a full description of each. (See pp. 91–92 and 100.)

BICEPS/TRICEPS CYCLE

The negative-only chin-up and the negative-only dip will add the finishing touches to your biceps and triceps. Chapter 5 details the correct performance of each movement. Make certain that you climb to the top position quickly, and lower your body weight slowly to the stretched position.

If you can do more than twelve slow repetitions in either the chin-up or the dip, you'll want to attach extra weight around your waist on your next workout.

SLOWLY AND SMOOTHLY

Your arms grow best by being overloaded intensely and briefly throughout a full-range of movement. To overload your arms efficiently, however, each repetition must be performed slowly and smoothly.

If you are in doubt about your speed of movement, always perform your repetitions slower—never faster—and your growth stimulation will accelerate.

CHAPTER ELEVEN

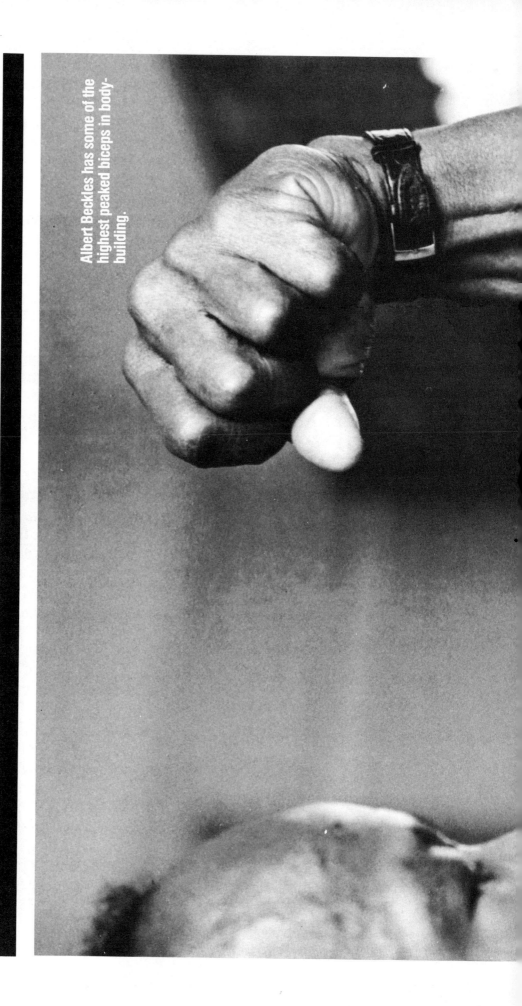

Albert Beckles has some of the highest peaked biceps in body-building.

The order of the exercises will be changed during Week 6. You'll be working your arms first, in a similar fashion as you did in Week 3.

During this week you'll also be training your arms only twice. Your legs and torso will receive the normal three-times-per-week workouts.

ROUTINE FOR WEEK 6
Week 6 provides one of the toughest routines in the program. Here's the way it breaks down:

Biceps Cycle
1. One-repetition chin-up (30–60 seconds raising and 30–60 seconds lowering), immediately followed by
2. Biceps curl

Triceps Cycle
3. One-repetition dip (30–60 seconds raising and 30–60 seconds lowering), immediately followed by
4. Triceps extension with one dumbbell held in both hands

Biceps/Triceps Cycle
5. Preacher curl, immediately followed by
6. Triceps pressdown on lat machine

7. Leg extension
8. Leg curl
9. Lateral raise with dumbbells
10. Bent-armed fly with dumbbells
11. Wrist curl
12. Reverse wrist curl

BICEPS AND TRICEPS CYCLES
Turn back to chapter 8 (pp. 89–92) and review the three upper-arm cycles. Perform

them once again in the same manner. You should be stronger now, so don't be afraid to use more resistance in each exercise. Applied properly, these three cycles should produce a terrific pump in your biceps and triceps.

LEG, TORSO, AND FOREARM EXERCISES
You should be familiar with the correct performance of the remaining six exercises. Push yourself to an all-out effort on each one.

Do not underestimate the importance of leg work. Remember: *If you want your arms to grow, work your legs*.

EVALUATING YOUR RESULTS
After your last workout of Week 6, take a full 48 hours of rest. Actually, 72 hours would be even better. While you are resting, review the measurement section in chapter 2 (p. 24). At the beginning of the following week, you'll want to take your after measurements, which include:

- Body weight
- Upper arms
- Forearms
- Chest
- Waist
- Thighs
- Body-fat percentage
- Photographs

Now, compare your after-measurements in each category to your before-measurements.

How did you do?

I'd be very surprised if you haven't added ⅝ inch on your best upper arm and ⅜ inch on your best forearm. Some trainees will add 1 inch or more on their upper arms; others will add ½ inch or less.

Your other circumference measurements should be greater, as well. You might want to compare your results with some of the increases from the Gainesville group in chapter 3.

If you've followed directions, trained intensely, and practiced good form—your results should be noteworthy.

WHAT TO DO NEXT
You've just completed a very intense six-week course for your arms. I do not recommend that you repeat the program too quickly. You would be well advised to practice a basic high-intensity schedule for at least three months. Such a basic schedule is described and illustrated in my book, *High-Intensity Bodybuilding*.

After three months of basic whole-body training, you may once again perform the program in *Big Arms in Six Weeks*.

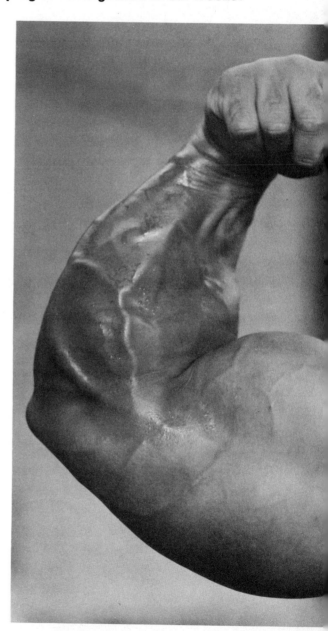

Above: The mighty arm of Tim Belknap. *Right:* Bill Grant's biceps muscles are extremely long, which accounts for much of his success at building big arms.

CHAPTER TWELVE

Vince Taylor displays a great set of arms.
Note especially his long biceps.

Realistic Goals & Conclusion

Notice that Sergio's left triceps lacks that traditional horseshoe shape. The reason is that the long head of triceps attaches farther down his arm than normal. This gives him a tremendous advantage in building mass.

"If you've followed directions, trained intensely, and practiced good form—your results should be noteworthy." Those words were in one of the final paragraphs of chapter 11.

It is important to mention that I did not say that your results from the six-week program would be *satisfying*. I said they would be *noteworthy*. And there's a big difference between the two concepts.

I've been bodybuilding since 1959. In my almost thirty years of experience, I've never met a bodybuilder who was *satisfied* with the results he was getting. Sure, you might be satisfied with (or envious of) your training partner's results, or someone else's gains, but not with your own.

Regardless of your progress you will always want more muscular size. That's natural and that's good—as long as you are realistic in dealing with your genetic potential.

GENETIC POTENTIAL

Arthur Jones said over fifteen years ago that most bodybuilders are not realistic in their goals. They want something that is beyond their genetic potential—namely great muscular size. In other words, their goal is simply not possible!

Jones went several steps further by saying that the major genetic factor behind great muscular size, especially in the arms, is extremely long muscle bellies in your biceps and triceps. And the length of your muscle bellies is 100 percent genetically determined. What you were born with is what you must live and die with.

Many of the bodybuilders featured in this book—especially Boyer Coe, Casey Viator, Sergio Oliva, Ed Robinson, and Arnold Schwarzenegger—have very long muscle bellies in their arms. It is no wonder that they have some of the biggest and best-shaped biceps and triceps in the world.

It is a known physiological fact that the longer a person's muscle, the greater the cross-sectional area and the overall volume of that muscle can become. Simple physiology reveals that for a muscle to be wide it has to be long. A short muscle could not be wide because its angle of pull would be so poor it would not be able to function efficiently. Thus, the body would not permit a short, wide muscle to exist.

How do you determine if you have long, average, or short muscle bellies in your upper arms?

The key factor is where your biceps and triceps muscles attach to the tendons that cross your elbow joints.

EVALUATING YOUR BICEPS POTENTIAL

Let's begin with the biceps. Take off your shirt and hit a double-biceps pose in front of a mirror. Look closely at the inside elbow area of both arms. Now, pronate (turn your hands away from your head) and supinate (turn your hands toward your head) your hands. Notice that when you supinate your hands, your biceps get more peaked. That's because the primary function of your biceps is supination of the hand.

Go back to the double-biceps pose with your hands fully supinated. The bend in your arms, or the angle between the bones in your upper arms and forearms should be 90 degrees. Look at the gap between your contracted biceps and elbow. How wide is the gap?

Before you measure it, relax your arms for a few minutes and while you're relaxing, do the following. Take your right hand and place your fingers and thumb across the crook of your left elbow. You should be able to feel the large tendon of the biceps as it crosses the front of the elbow joint and inserts into the radius bone of the forearm. In fact, as you gently contract your left biceps, dig your

finger tips into the elbow gap and get a good feel of the cablelike tendon. Follow the tendon up the arm until you feel where it connects to your biceps. It's the distance between where your biceps meets the tendon and where the tendon crosses the elbow joint that you need to determine.

Hit the double-biceps pose once again. Make sure your hands are fully supinated and that the bend in your arms is 90 degrees. Have a friend measure with a ruler the distance between the inside of your elbow (look for the crease in the skin on the front side of your elbow) and the inside edge of your contracted biceps. Do it for both your left and right arms.

What do the resulting figures mean?

Although this is certainly not an exact science by any means, my experience leads me to make the following generalizations:

Biceps Potential for Building Mass

Distance Between Elbow and Edge of Contracted Biceps	Biceps Length	Potential
½" or less	Long	Great
½"–1"	Above average	Good
1"–1½"	Average	Average
1½"–2"	Below average	Poor
2" or more	Short	Very minimal

Left: Look at the distance between Sergio's right elbow and his biceps: it's zero inches! Also notice how the belly of his right medial triceps runs almost to his elbow. *Above:* Casey Viator has long muscle bellies in his biceps and triceps, but not as long as Sergio's.

The bodybuilders with the really massive arms all have ½ inch or less distance between their elbows and contracted biceps. In other words, in their biceps they have long muscle bellies, short tendons, and great potential.

Sergio Oliva, the man with the most massive muscular arms in the world, has biceps muscles that are so long there are no gaps between his elbows and contracted biceps. That's right—no gaps, zero inches! As I stated in chapter 1, Sergio's arms would actually measure larger if he could fully contract his biceps by bending his elbows more. Sergio is one of the very few people in the world who has muscles that actually limit his range of movement. But even so, there are thousands of men today who would gladly trade their biceps for Sergio's.

While no one questions the importance of well-developed biceps, the muscle that contributes the most to the mass of the upper arm is the triceps.

EVALUATING YOUR TRICEPS POTENTIAL

The length of the triceps, compared to the biceps, is harder to determine. The difficulty lies in the fact that the junction between the three heads of the triceps and their common tendon is more difficult to measure and evaluate.

The triceps—as the name implies—is composed of three heads: lateral, long, and medial. All three heads attach to a large flat tendon that runs across the back of the elbow and connects to the forearm bone.

Take off your shirt again and look in the mirror. Turn to your side. With your elbow straight and your arm by your side, contract your triceps. You should observe, if you are reasonably lean, a distinct horseshoe shape to your triceps. The lateral head of your triceps forms one side of the horseshoe, the medial head forms the other side, the long head is at the top, and the tendon occupies the flat space in the middle.

What I've observed over many years is that the men with the really massive triceps have less and less of a horseshoe shape to the back of their arms. The flat space in the middle of the horseshoe is partially covered by the unusual length of the long head at the top. And the lateral and medial heads on the sides resemble upside-down soft drink bottles. What's left of the tendon is about the size of a rounded-off-at-one-end credit card.

Sergio Oliva, for example, has no horseshoe shape at all to the back of his arms. Bill Pearl's triceps are much the same as Sergio's, as are the triceps of Ray and Mike Mentzer.

To determine your triceps potential, here's what to do. With your elbow straight and your arm by your side, contract your triceps. Have a friend measure the distance from the tip of your elbow to the top of the inside of the horseshoe. In other words, you are measuring the longest portion of the flat tendon.

Remember, the longer the tendon, the shorter the muscle. Or the shorter the tendon, the longer the muscle.

Here are my generalizations for estimating your triceps potential:

Triceps Potential for Building Mass

Distance Between Elbow Tip and Top of Inside of Horseshoe	Triceps Length	Potential
3" or less	Long	Great
3"–4"	Above average	Good
4"–6"	Average	Average
6"–7"	Below average	Poor
7" or more	Short	Very minimal

You can still have a massive triceps—even if you have a short, long head—if your lateral and medial heads are long and thick. The triceps chart, therefore, is not as accurate as the biceps table.

My advice is to use both the biceps and the triceps charts in a very general, non-definitive manner.

Vincent Comerford's well-shaped biceps and triceps helped him win the middleweight class of the 1987 National Bodybuilding Championships.

Samir Bannout has only above-average length to his biceps and triceps. Even so, it did not keep him from winning Mr. Olympia.

The beautifully chiseled arms of
Bill Grant.

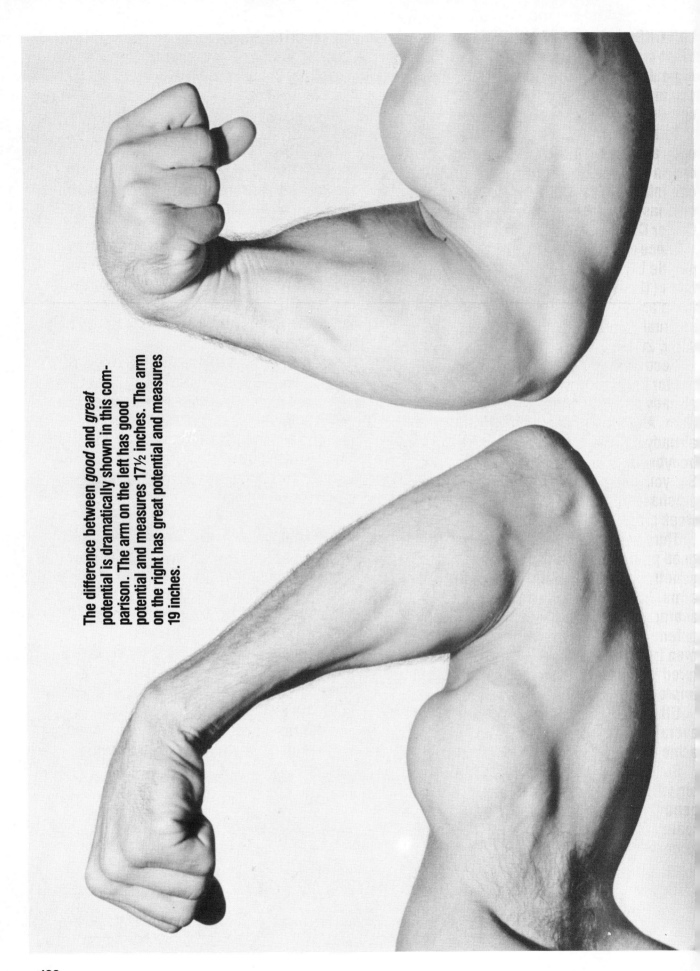

The difference between *good* and *great* potential is dramatically shown in this comparison. The arm on the left has good potential and measures 17½ inches. The arm on the right has great potential and measures 19 inches.

LOOKING AT THE PROBABILITIES

What are your chances for building a really big pair of arms? The type that would place you in the top five of the Mr. Olympia contest?

First, as you might already suspect, the odds are not good. At best they are perhaps one in a million. In other words, out of every one million men in the United States, only one has the potential to have arms like Boyer Coe or Casey Viator.

Since there are approximately 242 million people in the United States, and only half of them (121 million) are male, that means there are 121 males in this country with unusual genetic potential for building muscular, 20-inch arms.

Second, if you do have the genetic potential for building big arms, you probably already have big arms—even if you don't train. And if you do train, you probably already believe you understand the basics of bodybuilding because you have big arms. So, you would not have been motivated to purchase this book, nor adhere to this six-week program.

Thus, if you are reading this book, there is good probability that you do *not* have the genetic potential to build really exceptional arms. In fact, many of you probably have average, or slightly above-average, genetic potential. Many of you probably resemble the men from Gainesville, Florida, who are featured in chapter 3. If so, you can expect to improve at a rate similar to theirs.

Others of you will have much better-than-average genetic potential and you will achieve much better-than-average results.

But what can you ultimately become? How big will your arms be if you reach your genetic potential? In other words, what is a realistic goal for your upper arm circumference?

A REALISTIC GOAL

Joe Roark, whom I mentioned several times in chapter 2, lists the following formula for the average trainee:

To calculate your upper arm potential, multiply your wrist size in inches by 2.3.

For example, if your wrist size is exactly 7 inches, then 7 times 2.3 equals 16.1 inches. "But who wants a 16-inch arm?" you might be thinking.

Well, I promise you, a lean muscular 16-inch arm actually looks bigger than it is. In fact, of the ten participants in Gainesville that went through the program, only one, Craig Halladay, had an arm that measured more than 16 inches.

Furthermore, you've certainly got to get 16-inch arms before you move higher up the tape. And if you already have legitimate 16-inch arms, then your goal should be 17 inches. Or if you have 17-inch arms, then shoot for 18 inches.

In the final analysis, be realistic and take it one step at a time.

CONCLUSION

As I stated in chapter 1, "Don't expect your arms in six weeks to look like those of Boyer Coe, Casey Viator, or Sergio Oliva. But do expect your arms to be bigger, stronger, better shaped, and more defined."

Bigger, stronger, better shaped, and more defined arms are the result of hard, slow, strict, brief exercise—combined with adequate rest, recovery, and calories.

Be realistic in your expectations and your results may well exceed your goals.

Ed Robinson and friends enjoy some fresh air after a hard workout. Do not expect your arms to ever attain the mass of Ed Robinson's arms, unless you have similar genetic potential as he does. And be honest in your appraisal. Understand and apply the training principles in this book and soon your arms will be significantly BIGGER!